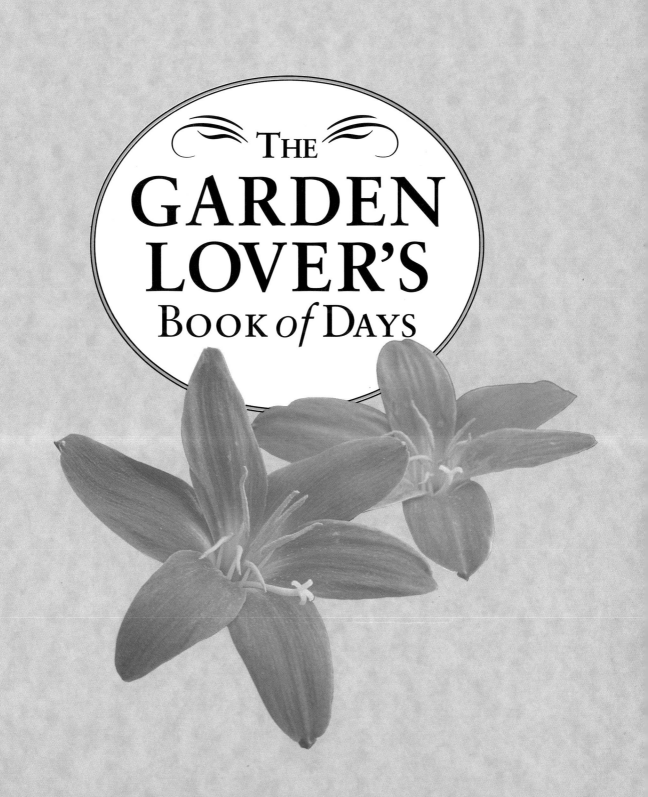

THE
GARDEN
LOVER'S
BOOK of DAYS

Photography
John Glover Photography
Neil Sutherland

Design
Paul Turner and Sue Pressley, Stonecastle Graphics Ltd
Marden, Kent

Editorial
Compiled and written by David Squire

Typesetting
DSP, Maidstone, Kent

Line artwork
John Hutchinson

Jacket
Photography: John Glover Photography
Design: Stonecastle Graphics Ltd

Production
Ruth Arthur
Sally Connolly

Director of production
Gerald Hughes

03192 The Garden Lover's Book of Days
This edition published in 1999 by CLB,
an imprint of Quadrillion Publishing Ltd

Distributed in the USA by
Quadrillion Publishing Inc.
230 Fifth Avenue, New York,
NY 10001

© 1993 Quadrillion Publishing Ltd,
Woolsack Way, Godalming,
Surrey, GU7 1XW, UK

ISBN 1-84100-281-X
Printed and bound in Spain

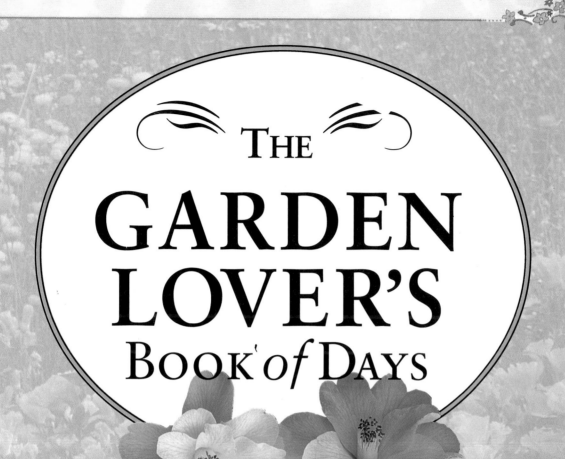

THE
GARDEN LOVER'S
BOOK *of* DAYS

CLB

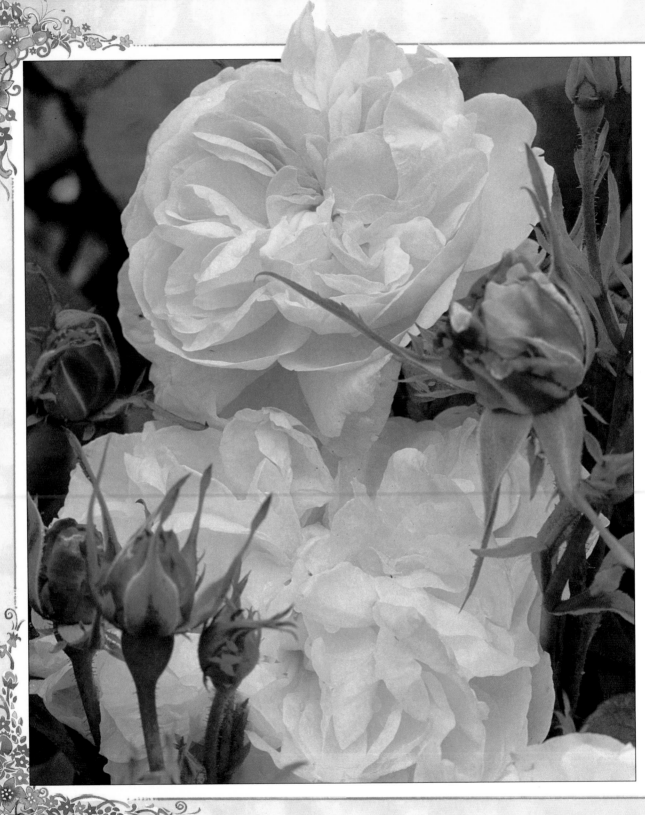

Introduction

Gardening is such an all-embracing hobby that reminders about what to do throughout the year are always welcome. Here, for every week of the year, there are suggestions about plants to buy for flower gardens or patios, how to create and improve lawns, grow vegetables, produce fruit and grow plants in greenhouses.

Because gardeners usually want to personalize their garden, making it different from and better than any other, it is necessary to make notes about varieties, planting schemes and ideas for improving the garden next year. Therefore, in this book there is space to make notes on each day of the year.

Few hobbies are so influenced by the capricious nature of the weather as gardening. Late spring frosts, summer storms, high winds in the fall, and sub-zero conditions in winter may cause annoyance but they seldom deter us from gardening.

There is also a weather pattern peculiar to your own garden. Bands of hills, proximity to the Gulf Stream, a southerly or northerly aspect and trees forming a shelter belt all influence local weather, and although frosts may occur in some northerly areas until as late as the first week in June, in the southwest they may be unknown throughout the winter. Therefore, it is necessary to understand your local weather patterns and to keep a few notes about it in this book. This information will better enable you to judge when to plant out frost-tender, summer-flowering bedding plants, put hanging-baskets outside on patios, prune roses, move late-flowering chrysanthemums into greenhouses in the fall, and so on.

Wild flower gardens are popular, and a range of native plants to create these areas is suggested on pages 152 and 153. They create bright, natural areas attractive to insects and birds, and some plants specifically attract butterflies and bees.

Encouraging birds into gardens is important and specific foods to attract them are also suggested.

To enable you to create a directory of gardening services, there is space at the back of this book for telephone numbers of local gardening services, such as garden centers, nurseries, fencing contractors, landscape designers, turfing services and tool rental stores. Once entered in this book, they will save you having repeatedly to search through directories, scraps of paper and old diaries.

This is not a diary just for one year, but a storehouse of general and personalized gardening information that can be added to from year to year.

January

January storms of wind and rain
Bring the bitter ice and snow
Yet even while the frosts remain
Under the trees the snowdrops glow

January

1

Seeds to sow this month are suggested throughout these pages

2

3

4

Don't use ashes or salt to clear paved paths of snow or ice as this damages plants set in crevices between the slabs.

5

6

Avoid treading on gardens unnecessarily when they are covered with snow. Lawn edges and plants can soon be damaged.

Flowers ▲
Make a note of areas in flower beds - as well as throughout the rest of the garden - that retain water. These may need to have rubble or tile drains installed when the weather allows.

Flowers
Gently remove snow from plants. If left, it weighs them down, sometimes breaking branches. Use a pole or piece of tubular plastic to tap and scrape it away. Clumps of bamboos are especially badly damaged by snow and unless this is quickly removed, it bends canes at ground level. ▼

7

There may be a garden society in your neighborhood which will provide useful advice about local soils and weather. Also, some societies offer garden materials and equipment at reduced costs.

Sweet Williams

Organic Gardening

When growing food for the home, select varieties that appeal to your family. Too often, varieties sold in stores are those that commercially are the easiest and most profitable to grow, last well while being transported and are eye-catching on shelves.

Lawns

Arrange to have the cutting blades on your lawn mower sharpened. Alternatively, sharpen the blades of hover-mowers yourself and check the cutting ability of rotary-mowers by passing a piece of paper between the blades. Have all electric cords and switching gear checked. Fit safety devices that instantly turn off the power if cords are damaged.

Fruit

When the weather allows, spray fruit trees with a tar-oil winter wash to kill overwintering eggs of pests. Thoroughly soak the trees. This also helps to remove algae.

Greenhouses

Water plants carefully in winter when they are not growing rapidly. If excessively watered, they wilt and their roots rot.

Plants from seeds

Most garden flowers raised from seeds are listed as herbaceous perennials, hardy annuals, half-hardy annuals or biennials. Although this gives an indication of the way they are increased, a few do not easily fit into these classifications. For example:

❀ English Daisies *(Bellis perennis)* and Sweet Williams *(Dianthus barbatus)* are hardy perennials grown as biennials.

❀ Lobelia *(Lobelia erinus)* is a half-hardy perennial grown as a half-hardy annual.

❀ Patience-plant *(Impatiens sultanii)* is a greenhouse perennial grown as a half-hardy annual.

❀ Snapdragons *(Antirrhinum majus)* are short-lived, woody perennials grown either as half-hardy annuals or hardy annuals.

❀ Sweet Alyssum *(Alyssum maritimum,* but now known as *Lobularia maritima)* is an annual usually grown as a half-hardy annual, but also as a hardy annual.

The sowing instructions recommended throughout this book are ways to increase plants and do not necessarily indicate a plant's normal nature.

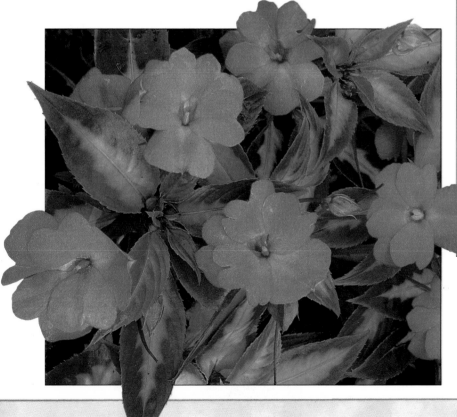

Patience-plant, a greenhouse perennial invariably grown as a long-lasting half-hardy annual, creates color throughout summer. It is important to keep these plants watered during dry weather.

8

9

Put both plastic and clay pots under cover. Plastic pots become brittle, while clay ones often crack when frozen.

10

11

This is often a month of reflection and looking forward to another season. Send away for seed and plant catalogs.

12

13

Ponds frequently become frozen, preventing fish gaining vital oxygen. Also, gases expelled by decaying vegetable material in the water become trapped under the ice. To free an area of ice, place a pot of boiling water on the surface. Depending on the thickness of the ice, the treatment may have to be repeated. Take care not to let the pot fall through the ice! Do not make a hole by hitting the ice, as this causes shock waves that may kill fish.

Flowers
Begin planning flower borders - both spring and summer-flowering bedding types as well as those for herbaceous plants. Sketch out the border's outline on graph paper, select plants and order them from seed companies and nurseries.

Greenhouses
Prepare for starting chrysanthemum stools (roots and woody bases) into growth to produce cuttings that will root and develop into plants for flowering later in the year. Initially, insure a supply of clean boxes, loam-based potting compost and labels.

14

Check greenhouse doors and ventilators to insure they fit properly. And have a few spare panes of glass in case of damage. Temporary repairs can be made with a piece of plastic sheeting secured in place to timber-framed greenhouses with wooden battens and nails.

Vegetables

Sow early cauliflowers in gentle warmth in a greenhouse to produce plants for planting in a vegetable bed in March or April. ▼

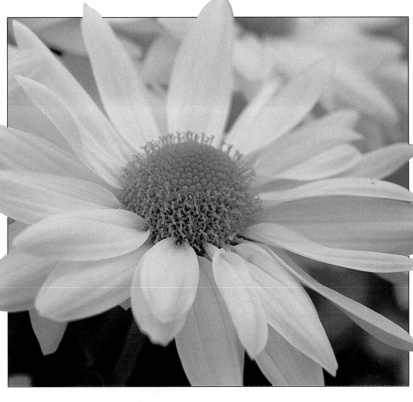

Organic Gardening

When creating a compost heap, beware of attracting rats and other vermin when putting out kitchen scraps, especially in winter. Make a wire-framed compost container with a meshed top, or use a proprietary type with a hinged lid.

Plants from seeds

❀ Herbaceous perennials die down to soil-level in the fall and send up fresh shoots in spring.

❀ Annuals grow from seeds, flower and die within the same year.

❀ Hardy annuals are sown outside in their flowering places.

❀ Half-hardy annuals are raised in gentle warmth early in the year and planted outside as soon as the risk of severe frost has passed. They then flower and die within the same year.

❀ Biennials are sown one year and flower during the following one. Seeds are sown in a seedbed, left to germinate, and the young plants are transferred to a nursery bed. In the fall - or early the following year - they are planted into their flowering positions.

Chrysanthemum "Rylite" is ideal in flower arrangements, as well as in gardens.

Right: Godetia "Sybil Sherwood" (bottom) and Coreopsis "Special Mixture".

January

15

16

17

18

When planning your garden, do not give tender plants an east-facing position. In winter, early-morning sun rapidly thaws frozen plants and damages them.

19

20

21

Some birds are beneficial to gardeners, eating grubs as well as small rodents. In winter, when natural food is scarce, they need to have their diet supplemented by gardeners (see pages 152 and 153 for details).

Flowers
Prepare the ground for dahlias, which are gross feeders and benefit from plenty of farmyard manure and compost. As well as providing plant foods, it helps to retain moisture in the soil.

Flowers ▲
When constructing a retaining wall, make the foundations strong and slightly slope the brickwork backward (as shown). Fill the space behind the wall with 12 inches of rubble. Also, every 5 feet along the wall's base insert pipes to enable water to escape.

Vegetables
Harvest winter cabbages as they mature.

From the end of July until the first frosts of the fall, dahlias create a riot of exciting colors.

Flowers grown as half-hardy annuals to sow this month in gentle warmth in a greenhouse

❀ Lobelia
   (Lobelia erinus)

❀ Petunia
   (Petunia x hybrida)

❀ Salvia
   (Salvia patens)

❀ Salvia
   (Salvia splendens)

Organic Gardening

Take care in winter when creating a bonfire not to incinerate hibernating animals. Don't just put a match to a pile of debris: instead, build a fresh heap several yards away, moving small amounts one at a time from the original heap.

Petunias, superbly colored annuals, are ideal in both hanging baskets and flower borders.

Fruit

Prune apple trees. Burn the prunings to prevent the spread of pests and diseases.

Greenhouses

Sow tomato seeds to produce plants for growing in greenhouses. Space the seeds about 1 inch apart, sowing them ¼ inch deep. Place them in 61°F and cover with a piece of glass. Invert the glass every day to prevent moisture falling on the compost, and remove as soon as the seeds germinate. ▼

January

22

23

When the north wind does blow,
We shall have snow.

24

25

Order seeds to avoid disappointment
later.

26

27

28

Construct and repair fences when the soil
can be walked on - not when frozen,
waterlogged or covered with snow. If this
job is left until spring, emerging bulbs
may be trodden on. Also, leaves and
stems obscure boundaries in spring and
summer. Additionally, it is easier to
knock stakes into damp soil than during
summer, when it may be dry and hard.

Flowers
Check dahlia tubers in store to insure
they are not wet and decaying.

Flowers
Insure chrysanthemum stools (cut down
plants) that were lifted in the fall and
packed in boxes with loam-based
compost around them have survived the
winter in a cold but frost-proof shed.

Vegetables ▲
Continue to harvest leeks, trimming the
roots and removing soil.

Vegetables
When harvesting trench celery, use a
trowel to move soil from around plants,
then a garden fork to ease them out of
the ground.

Fruit
If not completed, spray fruit trees with a
tar-oil winter wash. Insure the spraying
equipment is thoroughly cleaned after
use, then store it in a dry shed.

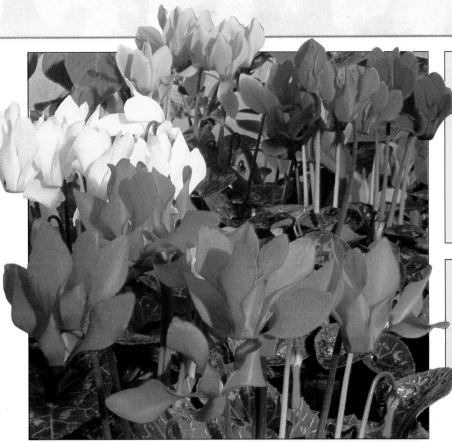

Flowers grown as half-hardy annuals to sow this month in gentle warmth in a greenhouse

❀ Slipper Flower
   (*Calceolaria integrifolia*)

❀ Snapdragon
   (*Antirrhinum majus*)

❀ Verbena
   (*Verbena x hybrida*)

Organic Gardening

Check fruit trees to insure all fruits from the previous year have been picked. If left on a tree, they encourage the presence of pests and diseases.

Left: Cyclamen are colorful houseplants.

Below: Slipper flowers are superb houseplants.

Fruit

Cut off sucker-like shoots from around the bases and stems of apple and pear trees. If they arise from the trunk, use a sharp knife to sever them flush with the bark. When growing from below ground level, remove soil and cut the shoot close to its point of origin.

Greenhouses

Sow cyclamen seeds for flowering during the following winter. Space out the seeds, using the point of a pencil or knife, and cover with ¼ inch of compost. Place in 55-61°F.

Greenhouses

The branches of trees and shrubs often encroach upon greenhouses, blocking out light. Cut off branches shading south sides, but leave trees on northerly and easterly aspects to create windbreaks from cold winds.

Above: Richly colored snapdragons are available in a wide range of colors and heights.

January

29

Lift parsnips, using a garden fork to ease them out of the soil.

30

Order seeds now for sowing in spring.

31

Order seed potatoes to avoid disappointment later.

If you have a spare piece of land - or wish to reduce the amount of formal garden - consider creating a wild-flower garden. Many seed companies offer wild flowers, singly or in mixtures, and include wild primroses, poppies, knapweed, wild pansies and wild cornflowers. ▼

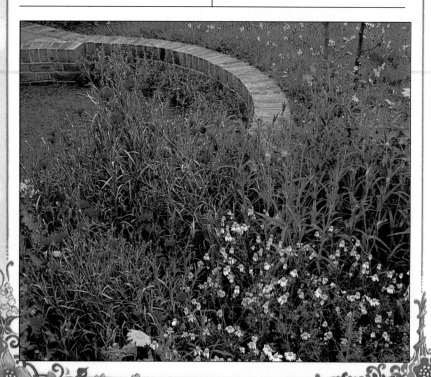

Flowers

Major changes to gardens are best undertaken during winter and until early spring, but not if the soil if frozen, waterlogged or covered in snow.

▲

Patio surfaces and paths, especially when in shade and with badly-drained surfaces, become covered with algae. Either remove it with copious amounts of water and a stiff brush, or spray with a tar-oil winter wash.

Greenhouses

Check the staging to insure it is secure. Water, humidity and strong sunlight throughout the year causes wood to deteriorate rapidly. Replace decayed wood and paint with an environmentally friendly wood preservative.

Greenhouses

If you have been growing tomatoes directly in border soil in a greenhouse - and their yield has slowly declined - dig out the soil and replace with fresh compost. Alternatively, grow plants in pots or growing-bags placed on the border soil.

Greenhouses

When buying houseplants, insure they are wrapped before leaving the nursery or garden center - and get them home rapidly. Do not buy houseplants that are displayed outdoors - they may not immediately show signs of distress, but later flower buds fall off and the plant collapses.

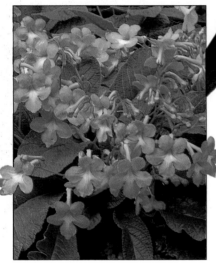

There are also white, rose to blue and purple varieties of Cape primrose.

An African Violet makes a perfect gift.

Organic Gardening

When selecting varieties of vegetables and fruits, choose those that are resistant to diseases and cultural problems. For instance, some vegetables are resistant to "bolting" (the premature development of flowering shoots and flowers), while others have a degree of resistance to rusts, mildew and viruses. Also, some vegetable varieties store better than others. Consult seed catalogs.

Common gloxinias need warmth and shade, as well as compost that is kept evenly moist.

Flowers to sow this month in gentle warmth to produce plants for greenhouses and home decoration

❀ African Violet
   (*Saintpaulia ionantha*)

❀ Cape Primrose
   (*Streptocarpus x hybridus*)

❀ Common Gloxinia
   (*Sinningia speciosa*)

❀ Cyclamen
   (*Cyclamen persicum*)

❀ Temple Bells
   (*Smithiantha cinnabarina*)

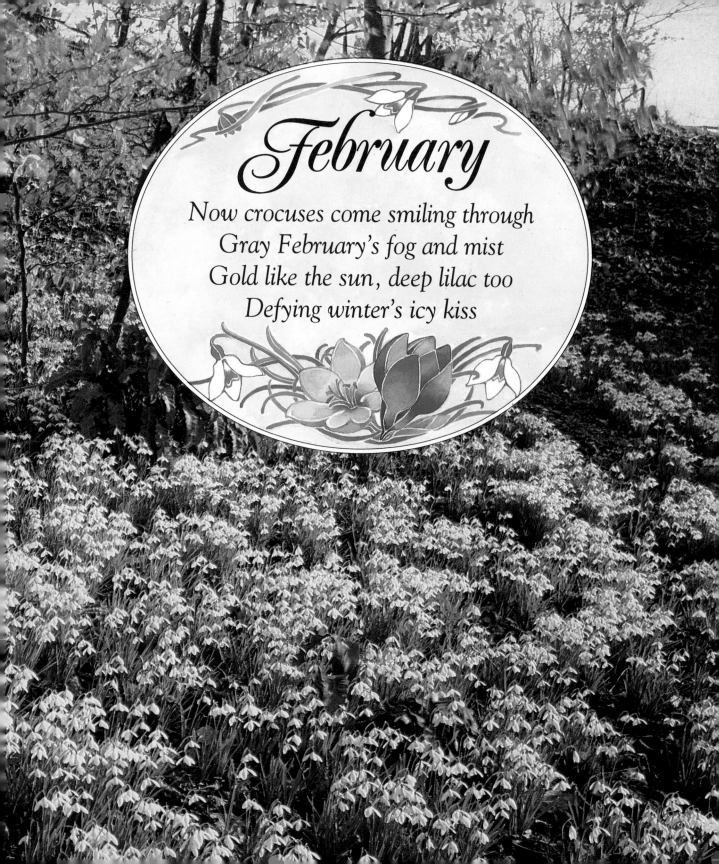

February

Now crocuses come smiling through
Gray February's fog and mist
Gold like the sun, deep lilac too
Defying winter's icy kiss

February

1

Sow seeds of greenhouse plants and houseplants, as indicated for this month.

2

3

4

As the outside temperature rises, increasingly open the ventilators on the leeside of your greenhouse. Avoid creating drafts.

5

6

7

Late winter is a time to review gardens and decide about further plants, perhaps a border packed with winter-flowering shrubs or one bursting with spring-flowering bulbs. These two features can be combined - bulbs grow well under deciduous shrubs, where they receive slight protection from frost in winter and have good light in spring.

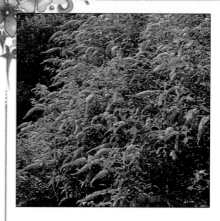

Flowers ▲

In mild areas, where the risk of further severe frost is not high, prune the orange-eye butterfly bush *(Buddleia davidii)*. Cut all the previous season's shoots back to within 2-3 inches of the old wood. This severe pruning encourages the development of strong shoots that will bear flowers during July and August.

Flowers

Gaps in beds of wallflowers can be filled by forking up and replanting a few of those planted around shrubs - or from spare plants earlier heeled-in in a nursery bed. Also, re-firm plants loosened by the action of frost.

Lawns ▲

Where stepping stones in lawns have settled below the surface, lift them and place sand underneath. Use a straight-edged board to check their height - flush with the surface of the lawn.

Vegetables
If not completed, dig vegetable plots, incorporating well-decomposed farmyard manure or garden compost. Remove and burn perennial weeds.

Greenhouses
Pack chrysanthemum stools in boxes of loam-based potting compost, water them and place in gentle warmth in a greenhouse.

Flowers to sow this month in gentle warmth to produce plants for greenhouse and home decoration

❀ African Violet
   (Saintpaulia ionantha)

❀ Cape Primrose
   (Streptocarpus hybridus)

❀ Common Gloxinia
   (Sinningia speciosa)

Phlox drummondii is an annual phlox with masses of colorful heads packed with pink, purple, lavender, red and white flowers from July through September. There are also herbaceous phloxes.

Greenhouses ▲
Put dahlia tubers into boxes, packing loam-based potting compost around their roots. Water and place them in gentle warmth in a greenhouse.

Flowers grown as half-hardy annuals to sow this month in gentle warmth in a greenhouse

❀ African Daisy
   (Arctotis x grandis)

❀ Ageratum
   (Ageratum houstonianum)

❀ American Marigold
   (Tagetes erecta)

❀ Annual Phlox
   (Phlox drummondii)

❀ Painted Gaillardia
   (Gaillardia pulchella)

❀ Shell Flower
   (Molucella laevis)

❀ Sweet Alyssum
   (Alyssum maritimum/Lobularia maritima)

❀ Touch-me-not
   (Impatiens balsamina)

February

8

Don't be frugal with half-hardy annuals - to create a stunningly attractive display in flower borders as well as in containers on a patio they must be planted densely. Therefore, raise plenty of plants by sowing seeds this month or during March.

9

10

11

A thornless climber, climbing rose is ideal for planting close to a doorway or path.

12

13

14

◄ Winter-flowering pansies need a bright, sunny position to encourage a wealth of flowers.

Flowers ▲
Create new rock gardens in sunny positions, not under trees. Shade, and leaves falling on plants in the fall, are detrimental, soon causing them to deteriorate. Also, insure the area is well drained. The stones must slightly tilt backward. If you do not have space for a rock garden, you could build a dry-stone wall. It is surprising how many plants can be set in it.

Flowers
If herbaceous plants have not yet been tidied up and old shoots cut down, do this now. Also, fork lightly between plants, spreading well-rotted manure or compost between them.

Rock gardens create homes for alpines, bulbs, dwarf conifers and small herbaceous plants. Do not position rock gardens under trees.

Lawns
Where daffodils are naturalized in lawns, cordon off the area to protect the emerging shoots.

Vegetables
When starting a new vegetable garden, first dig the site, remove and burn all perennial weeds. Then, plant a crop of potatoes, setting the tubers 6 inches deep, 2 feet apart and in rows with 2-2½ feet between them. Prepare the soil now and plant the potatoes in spring. Using potatoes in this way helps to clear the land of weeds, and to break up the soil.

Vegetables
Create a summer screen – as well as an edible one – by sowing a double line of runner bean seeds. Seeds cannot be sown until all risk of frost has passed, but now is the time to prepare the soil. Dig out a trench 12-15 inches deep and fill its base with well-decayed farmyard manure or garden compost. This helps to retain moisture around the roots. Moisture and sunshine are essential.

Fruit
If you want a plum tree but have space for only one tree, select 'Victoria'. It is self-fertile and good for both cooking and eating.

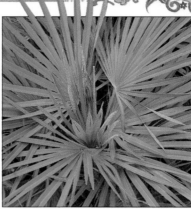

Windwill palms can be grown outdoors.

Palms to sow this month in warmth for home and conservatory decoration

- ❀ Areca Palm
  (*Chrysalidocarpus lutescens*)
- ❀ Californian Fan Palm
  (*Washingtonia filifera*)
- ❀ Canary Island Date Palm
  (*Phoenix canariensis*)
- ❀ Date Palm
  (*Phoenix dactilifera*)
- ❀ Mediterranean Palm
  (*Chamaerops humilis*)
- ❀ Windmill Palm
  (*Trachycarpus fortunei*)

Fruit
A shortage of lime in the soil when growing plums, cherries and peaches causes poor pit development. Therefore, before planting these fruits, insure the soil is slightly alkaline. An inexpensive soil-testing kit will indicate its alkalinity or acidity.

Greenhouses
When buying a greenhouse, work out the size you need, then double it. You will always need more space than initially anticipated.

Flowers grown as half-hardy annuals to sow this month in gentle warmth in a greenhouse

- ❀ Canary Bird Flower
  (*Tropaeolum perigrinum*)
- ❀ Common Stock
  (*Matthiola incana*)
- ❀ French Marigold
  (*Tagetes patula*)
- ❀ Heliotrope
  (*Heliotropium x hybridum*)
- ❀ Kingfisher-daisy
  (*Felicia bergerana*)
- ❀ Livingstone Daisy
  (*Dorotheanthus bellidiformis*)
- ❀ Lobelia
  (*Lobelia erinus*)
- ❀ Nemesia
  (*Nemesia strumosa*)

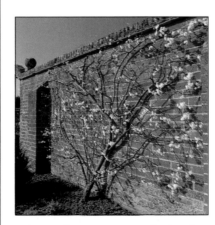

Plums can be grown against a wall, where they benefit from the warmth and shelter.

February

15

16

17

18

Keep lawns short throughout the year to minimize the risk of children becoming infected with *Toxicara*, a parasite transmitted by dogs and cats.

19

20

Continue to sow tomato seeds to raise plants for growing in greenhouses.

21

Rose bushes affected by black spot last year should be tidied up by removing and burning all leaves from around them.

Flowers

Prune winter jasmine (*Jasminum nudiflorum*) as soon as its flowers fade. Cut back flowered shoots to 2-3 inches of their bases. Completely cut out old and weak wood.

Flowers ▲

Romantic, scent-enriched bowers should be planned now. Many roses, as well as several clematis, are scented and will create leafy and floriferous overhead canopies. Use scented annuals to produce scent around its base. Either construct a rustic arch against a wall, or form an arbor with brick pillars and wooden cross beams.

Flowers

Trim winter-flowering heathers as soon as their flowers fade. Use hedge shears to clip lightly over them, creating a gently undulating surface.

Vegetables ▲
Place cloches along rows where vegetable seeds are to be sown later in the year. This insures that the soil will be warm and germination rapid. Use glass or plastic to close the ends of the cloches to avoid creating a cold, drafty tunnel.

Fruit ▲
Spray peach trees and nectarines against peach leaf curl, a disease that causes leaves to thicken, first becoming greenish-yellow, then deep-crimson.

Fruit
Inspect fruits in store, removing those that show signs of decay. If left, they cause other fruits to deteriorate.

Flowers to sow this month in gentle warmth to produce plants for greenhouse and home decoration

❀ German Violet
  (Exacum affine)

❀ Temple Bells
  (Smithiantha cinnabarina)

❀ Top Primrose
  (Primula obconica)

Top primroses flower from December through May in greenhouses as well as indoors.

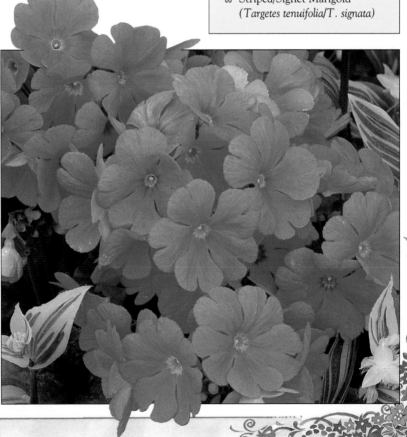

Flowers grown as half-hardy annuals to sow this month in gentle warmth in a greenhouse

❀ Blue Lace Flower
  (Didiscus ceruleus/Trachymene ceruleu)

❀ Cockscomb
  (Celosia plumosa)

❀ Dusty Miller
  (Chrysanthemum ptarmicaeflorum)

❀ Heartleaf Maskflower
  (Alonsoa warscewiczii)

❀ Petunia
  (Petunia x hybrida)

❀ Salvia
  (Salvia splendens)

❀ Striped/Signet Marigold
  (Targetes tenuifolia/T. signata)

February

22

23

For a fast-growing hedge, plant Leyland cypress (*Cupressocyparis leylandii*), but remember that when established it grows several feet a year and eventually reaches over 50 feet high and 15 feet wide. It is best as a windbreak and planted at least 100 feet from a house.

24

25

26

27

28/29

Pot cuttings of perpetual-flowering carnations. Do not keep them in high temperatures.

Flowers
In warm areas, prune shrubs that flowered late during the previous summer. Pruning now encourages the development of shoots that will bear flowers later in the year.

Flowers
Clean out water-butts, especially if leaves have fallen in them. Tip the barrel over and scrub the inside. Warm water, disinfectant and a scrubbing brush usually removes algae and slime. Afterwards, thoroughly rinse with water.

Vegetables
If, after clearing your garden shed, you have amassed chemicals which you don't want, do not tip them down a drain as they may contaminate water courses. Instead, consult your town council.

Vegetables ▲
Feed established asparagus beds with a general fertilizer at ½ cup/square yard.

Fruit ▲
Prune fall-fruiting raspberries now. Cut the canes to within a few inches of the ground.

Fruit
When inserting wooden posts to support fences or fruit canes, first place their bases in deep plastic bags that rise about 6 inches above the soil. Tie each bag's top closely to its stake. And insure that a "cap" is nailed to the top of the post to prevent water entering the wood.

Greenhouses
Pot the tuber-like, scaly rhizomes of achimines, five or six to a 5 inch pot, using a loam-based potting compost. Set the rhizomes about 1inch deep, water and place the pots in 61°F. Increase the amount of water as shoots develop.

Palms to sow this month in warmth for home and conservatory decoration

❀ Mexican Fan Palm
   (*Washingtonia robusta*)

❀ Paradise Palm
   (*Howea forsterana*)

❀ Parlor Palm
   (*Chamaedorea elegans*)

❀ Pigmy Date Palm
   (*Phoenix roebelenii*)

Flowers grown as half-hardy annuals to sow this month in gentle warmth in a greenhouse

❀ Bedding Begonias
   (*Begonia semperflorens*)

❀ Flowering Tobacco
   (*Nicotiana alata affinis*)

❀ Snapdragon
   (*Antirrhinum majus*)

❀ Slipper Flower
   (*Calceolaria integrifolia*)

❀ Spider Flower
   (*Cleome spinosa*)

❀ Tassel Flower
   (*Emilia flammea*)

❀ Verbena
   (*Verbena x hybrida*)

Bedding begonias are superb in summer displays. They can also be planted in window-boxes, troughs and around the edges of tubs on patios.

Flowering tobacco has an intense evening scent.

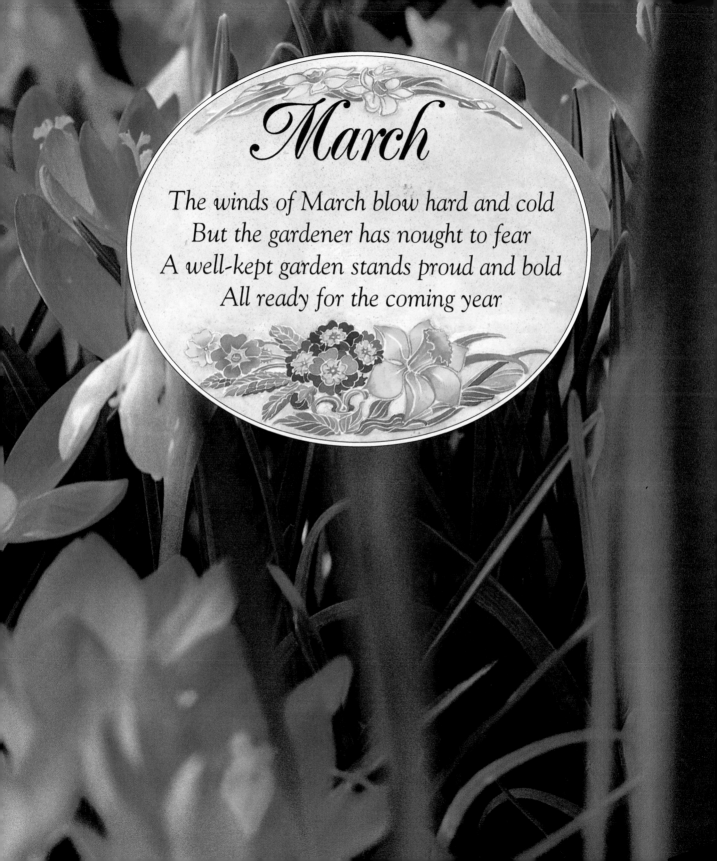

March

The winds of March blow hard and cold
But the gardener has nought to fear
A well-kept garden stands proud and bold
All ready for the coming year

March

1

*For every fog in March,
There'll be a frost in May.*

2

Sow sweet pea seeds ½ inch deep in seedtrays and place in 61-68°F. They can also be sown outdoors in April in the garden.

Sweet peas are some of the loveliest flowers for decorating rooms in summer.

3

Sow celery seeds in boxes or pots in greenhouses, placing them in 55-61°F.

4

5

6

7

 When buying houseplants, avoid those with roots coming out of drainage holes in their pots. Also, do not buy plants with pots covered with moss or algae, flowers fully open, or stems bare of leaves. Additionally, discard large plants in small pots or small plants in large pots.

Flowers

Plant container-grown shrubs at any time when the soil is not frozen or waterlogged. Prepare the planting site, forking-in a light dressing of bonemeal. Dig out a hole large enough to accommodate the container, and form a small mound of soil in its base. Water the plant a few hours before setting it in the soil. Remove the container and spread out the roots, with the top of the soil-ball slightly lower than the surrounding soil. It may be necessary to adjust the height of the mound. Firm soil around the roots.

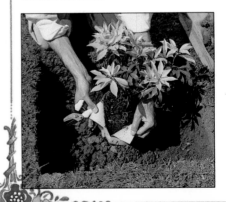

Flowers to sow this month in gentle warmth to produce plants for greenhouse and home decoration

- ❀ African Violet
  (*Saintpaulia ionantha*)
- ❀ Cape Primrose
  (*Streptocarpus hybridus*)
- ❀ Kalanchoe
  (*Kalanchoe blossfeldiana*)
- ❀ Top Primrose
  (*Primula obconica*)

Pink-mauve ageratums complement deep-violet petunias.

Flowers
Do not leave foliage houseplants continually in one position, as leaves and stems grow toward the light and eventually create an unsightly plant. Instead, turn the plant a quarter of a turn every few days.

Lawns
Grass cutting begins soon. For the first cut, set the blades high, gradually reducing their height as the season progresses.

Below left: When planting container-grown shrubs, take care when removing the container not to damage the plant's roots.
Below: After putting the plant in the hole and covering with soil, gently use your foot to firm soil around the roots.

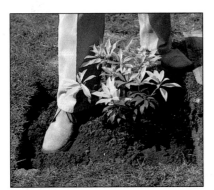

Vegetables
From now and until May, sow radishes thinly in drills ½ inch deep and 10 inches apart.

Vegetables ▲
Sow parsnip seeds in groups of three, 6-8 inches a part, ½ inch deep and in drills 15 inches apart. These are later thinned to the strongest seedling at each position.

Greenhouses
Take chrysanthemum cuttings, 2½-3 inches long. Remove the lower leaves, trim beneath a leaf-joint and insert ¾-1 inch deep in equal parts moist peat and sharp sand. Water and place in gentle warmth.

Flowers grown as half-hardy annuals to sow this month in gentle warmth in a greenhouse

- ❀ African Daisy
  (*Arctotis grandis*)
- ❀ Ageratum
  (*Ageratum houstonianum*)
- ❀ American Marigolds
  (*Tagetes erecta*)
- ❀ Annual Phlox
  (*Phlox drummondii*)
- ❀ Globe Amaranth
  (*Gomphrena globosa*)
- ❀ Painted Gaillardia
  (*Gaillardia pulchella*)
- ❀ Shell Flower
  (*Molucella laevis*)
- ❀ Sweet Alyssum
  (*Alyssum maritimum/Lobularia maritima*)
- ❀ Touch-me-not
  (*Impatiens balsamina*)
- ❀ Transvaal Daisy
  (*Gerbera jamesonii*)

8

9

March winds and April showers,
Bring forth May flowers.

10

11

Sow onion seeds thinly in drills ½ inch
deep and 9-12 inches apart.

12

13

14

◀ Giving houseplants the exact amount of
water they need is difficult, but using
moisture-indicator strips helps to make
this job easier.

Flowers ▲

Lift and divide large, congested clumps
of herbaceous plants. Use a garden fork
to dig under the clump and to prize it
gently apart. Replant young parts from
around the outside. Discard the old,
woody, central parts.

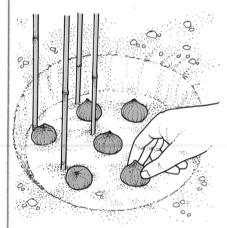

Flowers ▲

Plant gladioli (5-6 inches deep) in small
groups, each corm about 8 inches apart.
Before covering, insert stakes by the side
of each corm.

Flowers

Plant *Ranunculus asiaticus* tubers 2 inches
deep) and lily bulbs (usually about
two-and-a-half times their depth) if the
soil is workable. However, the
Madonna lily (*Lilium candidum*) is
planted with its nose just below the
surface.

Lawns

Repair edges, especially where soil has fallen against the lawn.

Vegetables

Sow fava beans 3 inches deep and 8 inches apart in drills 10-12 inches apart. Usually, they are sown in double rows, with a 2 feet wide path between each pair.

Fruit

Soft fruits can still be planted. Also, check plants put in earlier, re-firming soil loosened by frost.

Greenhouses

Take cuttings of pelargoniums. Trim off the lower leaves, cutting stems below leaf-joints and inserting them into sandy compost. Place in gentle warmth.

Greenhouse

Take cuttings of dahlias, fuchsias and perpetual-flowering carnations.

The trumpet-shaped Lilium candidum *is one of the most spectacular lilies for garden display.*

Above: A beautiful variety of pelargonium, aptly named 'Jewel'.

Below: The exquisite fuchsia 'Perky Pink', an undeniably beautiful plant.

Flowers grown as half-hardy annuals to sow this month in gentle warmth in a greenhouse

- ❀ Canary Bird Flower
  (*Tropaeolum peregrinum*)

- ❀ China Aster
  (*Callistephus chinensis*)

- ❀ Common Stock
  (*Matthiola incana*)

- ❀ French Marigold
  (*Tagetes patula*)

- ❀ Heliotrope
  (*Heliotropium x hybridum*)

- ❀ Kingfisher-daisy
  (*Felicia bergerana*)

- ❀ Livingstone Daisy
  (*Dorotheanthus bellidiformis*)

- ❀ Lobelia
  (*Lobelia erinus*)

- ❀ Nemesia
  (*Nemesia strumosa*)

Organic Gardening

Gardens that attract butterflies are popular. In spring, *Alyssum saxatile*, aubrietia and forget-me-nots are appealing to them.

15

16

Sow carrots thinly in drills ½-¾ inch deep and 9 inches apart.

17

18

Sow early peas, 4 inches apart in drills 2 inches deep.

19

20

21

Dahlia 'Shoesmith Salmon'

Flowers
In mild areas, plant dahlia tubers that have been stored during winter but have not developed shoots. Cover the tubers with 3 inches of soil.

Flowers
Remove glass tents and cloches earlier put over alpine plants to prevent rain damaging them. Wear gloves and place the glass where it will not be a danger to animals or children.

Lawns
Brush and scatter worm casts. If left and trodden on they create muddy patches and kill grass seedlings.

Vegetables
Plant young cauliflowers raised from seeds sown in a greenhouse in January. Plant them 2 feet apart in rows 2 feet apart. Insure the soil is well firmed around their roots.

◀ If a houseplant wilts because the compost is dry, revive it by standing the pot in a bowl of water. Also, mist-spray plants with smooth-surfaced leaves.

Fruit

Place cloches over a few strawberry plants to encourage early fruiting. It also prevents rain damaging the fruits.

Greenhouses

Pot up cyclamen seedlings. The corms must be at compost level - if excessively deep they will not develop properly, but if too high they become dry and hard.

Greenhouses

Plant common gloxinia (*Sinningia*) tubers, setting them slightly apart and packing moist peat around them. Water and place them in gentle warmth. When shoots appear, pot them into small pots.

Flowers to sow this month in gentle warmth to produce plants for greenhouse and home decoration

- ❀ Common Gloxinia
  (*Sinningia speciosa*)
- ❀ German Violet
  (*Exacum affine*)
- ❀ Temple Bells
  (*Smithiantha cinnabarina*)

Cockscomb creates fluffy spires in pink, yellow, crimson and amber.

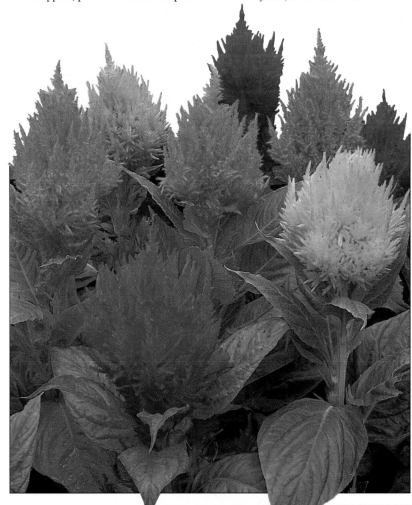

Flowers grown as half-hardy annuals to sow this month in gentle warmth in a greenhouse

- ❀ Blue Lace Flower
  (*Didiscus caeruleus*)
- ❀ Cockscomb
  (*Celosia plumosa*)
- ❀ Feverfew
  (*Chrysanthemum parthenium*)
- ❀ Heart leaf Mask-flower
  (*Alonsoa warscewiczii*)
- ❀ Petunia
  (*Petunia x hybrida*)
- ❀ Prince's Feather
  (*Amaranthus hypochondriacus*)
- ❀ Salvia
  (*Salvia splendens*)
- ❀ Silver Lace
  (*Chrysanthemum ptarmicaeflorum*)
- ❀ Striped/Signet Marigold
  (*Tagetes tenuifolia/T. signata*)

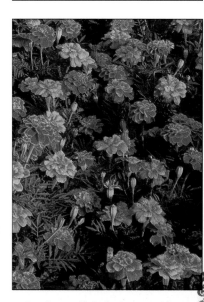

French marigold "Sophia" grows in full sun.

March

22

23

Continue to take cuttings of dahlias.

24

Remove dead flower heads from bulbs that have flowered. If left, they produce seeds at the expense of bulb development.

25

26

27

28

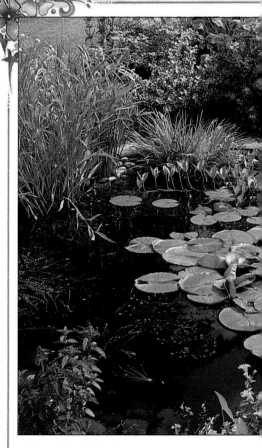

Above: A pond often forms a centerpiece in a garden and seldom fails to capture attention. Do not position it under trees.

Repot all plants that fill their pots with roots.

Ponds
Garden ponds are eye-catching features. They are usually created from either a rigid glassfiber shell, which is set in a hole dug to fit it, or a flexible plastic liner. The quality and thickness of the liner determines its life span.

Flowers ▷
Small baskets planted with pansies, polyanthas, small-leaved and variegated ivies, heathers and cyclamineus-type narcissi create displays ideal for sheltered patios and cold porches. Keep the compost moist, but not continually saturated.

Flowers

Plant bare-rooted rose bushes. Unpack the plants and stand them in water. Trim off damaged roots and cut back long shoots to outward-pointing buds. Position them in the ground so that the old soil-mark on the stem is fractionally below the surface. This allows for soil settlement. Firm soil around the roots.

Vegetables

In mild areas, plant early potatoes, 6 inches deep and 12 inches apart in rows 2 feet apart. In cold areas, delay planting for three or four weeks.

Vegetables △

Plant onion sets 4-6 inches apart in rows 12 inches apart. The necks of the sets must be just above the soil's surface.

Flowers grown as half-hardy annuals to sow this month in gentle warmth in a greenhouse

❀ Bedding Begonias
  (*Begonia semperflorens*)

❀ Flowering Tobacco
  (*Nicotiana alata affinis*)

❀ Mexican Fire Bush
  (*Kochia scoparia trichophylla*)

❀ Snapdragon
  (*Antirrhinum majus*)

❀ Slipper Flower
  (*Calceolaria integrifolia*)

❀ Spider Flower
  (*Cleome spinosa*)

❀ Tassel Flower
  (*Emilia flammea*)

❀ Verbena
  (*Verbena x hybrida*)

❀ Zinnia
  (*Zinnia elegans*)

Greenhouses

Prick out young seedlings before they become congested. Hold each seedling by one of its leaves, not its stem. And do not allow their roots to become dry.

Greenhouses

Increase the amount of ventilation but avoid creating drafts. Open the ventilators on the leeside. Automatic ventilators help to make this job easier.

Greenhouses

Increase the amount of water given to plants in pots in greenhouses and indoors. But insure the compost is not continually saturated as this kills roots. If the compost does become waterlogged, remove the pot and wrap a dish cloth around the soil-ball. When dry, repot in a clean pot.

March

29

30

March comes in like a lion, goes out like a lamb.

31

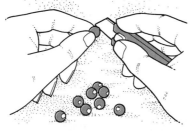

When sowing large seeds with hard coats, such as sweet peas, either nick the seed's coat with a sharp knife or scrape with a nail-file. This allows the seed readily to absorb moisture, an essential stage in germination.

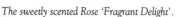

The sweetly scented Rose 'Fragrant Delight'.

Flowers ▲
When pruning roses, always cut fractionally above an outward-pointing bud. If long snags are left, this encourages the onset of decay, while if too close there is the risk of the bud being damaged.

Flowers
Prune hybrid tea (large-flowered roses) and floribunda (cluster-flowered roses) now.

Apple trees following the line of a curved garden wall. Trees trained in this way should have their blossom protected from severe frosts.

Hardy annuals to sow outdoors this month, where they are to flower

❀ Annual Chrysanthemum
(*Chrysanthemum carinatum/C. tricolor*)

❀ California Poppy
(*Eschscholzia californica*)

❀ Clarkia
(*Clarkia elegans*)

❀ Clarkia
(*Clarkia pulchella*)

❀ Convolvulus
(*Convolvulus tricolor/C.minor*)

❀ Cornflower
(*Centaurea cyanus*)

❀ Larkspur
(*Delphinium ajacis*)

❀ Love-lies-Bleeding
(*Amaranthus caudatus*)

❀ Oriental Woodruff
(*Asperula azurea-setosa*)

❀ Pot Marigold
(*Calendula officinalis*)

❀ Summer Adonis
(*Adonis aestivalis*)

❀ Swan River Daisy
(*Brachycome iberidifolia*)

❀ Viper's Bugloss
(*Echium lycopsis*)

❀ Winter Cape-marigold
(*Dimorphotheca aurantica*)

Convolvulus can be sown outdoors this month, where it is to flower. Any well-drained garden soil will do. Choose a sunny situation.

Lawns
Use a lawn roller to level turf slightly lifted by frost. However, do not expect a roller to level large mounds. Remember that rolling consolidates soil and restricts aeration.

Vegetables
Prick out celery seedlings sown earlier in the year in a greenhouse. Space them 2 inches apart. Leave the seedbox in gentle warmth in a greenhouse for a week, then place in a cold frame, slowly hardening off the plants.

Fruit
Protect blossoms on wall-trained fruit trees if frost is expected. Either hook up or tie dry hessian or sacks over the flowers or, if low, place a cold frame over them.

Greenhouses
Harden off sweet peas sown earlier in the year in a greenhouse. Reduce temperature, then put them in a cold frame.

April

Spring-like sunshine arrives at last
As April days now warm the earth
Cruel winter is but a memory past-
Once again the world gives birth

April

1

2

A red sky in the morning,
Is a shepherd's warning,
A red sky at night,
Is a shepherd's delight.

3

4

April showers bring forth May flowers.

5

6

Plant greenhouse tomato plants in the border soil, growing-bags or pots.

7

Patio tubs packed with bright-faced polyanthus - perhaps encircling a yellow-foliaged, cone-shaped dwarf conifer - bring a burst of spring color to patios. These plants can be set in a tub now.

Flowers ▲
As early daffodils fade, remove the flower heads but leave their leaves intact. Allow them to die down naturally. To keep them tidy, bend their leaves over and secure with elastic bands or twine. Alternatively, tie in knots.

Lawns
Prepare sites in readiness for sowing seeds. If the area is wet and sticky, leave this job until the end of the month. Dig the site - if not previously undertaken in winter - and break up the soil. Rake level, removing stones of more than 1 inch in size. Leave smaller ones, as they assist in drainage. Insure all perennial weeds have been removed. Check that the site is level - or evenly sloped - by knocking pegs into the ground and placing a spirit-level across them.

Vegetables
Prepare a seedbed by digging the soil, then lightly consolidating and levelling it. Then sow Brussels sprouts seeds. Later, transplant them to their growing positions.

Fruit trees
Prune plums and greengages as soon as their sap starts to rise. If pruned in winter, when dormant, there is a risk of diseases entering cuts.

Herb tree mallow is an annual.

Flowers to sow this month in gentle warmth to produce plants for greenhouse and home decoration

❀ Cineraria
(*Senecio cruentus*)

❀ German Violet
(*Exacum affine*)

❀ Kalanchoe
(*Kalanchoe blossfeldiana*)

❀ Temple Bells
(*Smithiantha cinnabarina*)

❀ Top Primrose
(*Primula obconica*)

Hardy annuals to sow outdoors this month, where they are to flower

❀ Annual Chrysanthemum
(*Chrysanthemum carinatum*)

❀ Baby Blue Eyes
(*Nemophila menziesii*)

❀ Baby's Breath
(*Gypsophila elegans*)

❀ California Poppy
(*Eschscholzia californica*)

❀ Herb Tree-mallow
(*Lavatera trimestris*)

❀ Oriental Woodruff
(*Asperula orientalis*)

Fruit trees

Spray fruit trees and bushes with pesticides and insecticides before bud-burst or after petal-fall. This helps to reduce the number of pollinating insects killed by chemical sprays.

Greenhouses ▲

If congested with seedlings and newly sown seedboxes, make more space in greenhouses by the addition of temporary shelves suspended from wires attached to the glazing bars. But take care, as they may easily be tipped over. Additionally, insure that when watering plants on these shelves, moisture does not drip on those below. Special shelving can be bought for fixing to aluminum greenhouses.

Above: Baby's breath is peppered with flowers.

Left: Cinerarias are ideal houseplants.

Organic Gardening

Ladybug larvae and adults eat greenfly (aphids). Lacewings and hoverflies also kill this major pest. Therefore, encourage these natural predators by not indiscriminately spraying them with insecticides.

April

8

9

Rain before seven,
Fine before eleven.

10

11

It is not spring until you can plant your foot
upon twelve daisies.

12

13

There's rosemary, that's for remembrance;
pray, love, remember:
and there is pansies,
that's for thoughts.
William Shakespeare - Hamlet

14

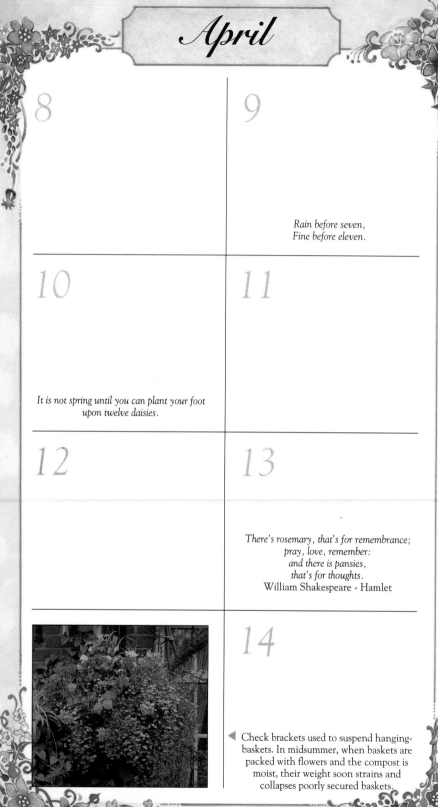

◀ Check brackets used to suspend hanging-
baskets. In midsummer, when baskets are
packed with flowers and the compost is
moist, their weight soon strains and
collapses poorly secured baskets.

Flowers
Prune winter-flowering shrubs now, and
spring-flowering types as soon as their
flowers fade. Winter-flowering shrubs
require little pruning, other than the
removal of dead or damaged shoots, as
well as tidying up the plant's shape.

Spring-flowering shrubs, however,
need more extensive pruning. Because
their flowers are borne mainly on shoots
which developed during the middle or
late part of the previous season, cut out a
few of the oldest shoots from the base.
This encourages the development of
fresh shoots that will bear flowers during
the following spring. Also, remove dead
wood and twiggy growths from the
plant's center.

Lawns
Soil preparation for seed sowing can be
completed now. To consolidate the soil
evenly, systematically tread over it,
shuffling sideways across the plot and
each time firming a strip about
10 inches wide. Rake the surface level
and add a general fertilizer, mixing it
into the top 1 inch. The same thorough
soil preparation is needed for
sowing seeds and when laying turf.

Left: Colorful poppies which, despite their delicate appearance, do not need staking. It is necessary, however, to remove dead flowers to prevent them scattering seeds.

Hardy annuals to sow outdoors this month, where they are to flower

❀ Clarkia
   (*Clarkia elegans*)

❀ Flanders Field Poppy
   (*Papaver rhoeas*)

❀ Flower-of-an-Hour
   (*Hibiscus trionum*)

❀ Godetia
   (*Godetia grandiflora*)

❀ Annual Larkspur
   (*Consolida ambigua*)

❀ Love-in-a-Mist
   (*Nigella damascena*)

Below: Stately larkspur, whose long-lasting flowers are ideal for flower arrangements.

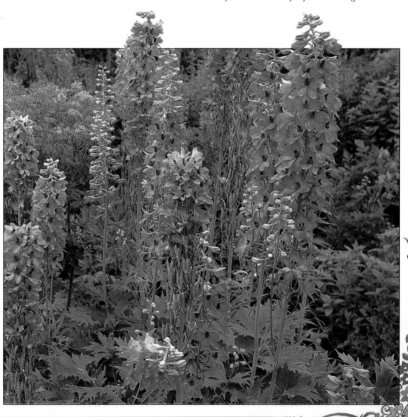

Vegetables △
Sow seeds of cabbages for harvesting during summer and fall. Sow seeds ¾ inch deep in drills 6 inches apart in a seedbed. The young plants are later planted in a vegetable garden.

Vegetables
Sow parsley seed in pots, then place in 50-59°F.

Greenhouses
Cyclamen plants that have finished flowering need drying. Place the pots on their sides under the greenhouse staging, in a dry place.

April

15

16

Clear moon, frost soon

17

18

Prepare new asparagus beds - dig trenches
15 inches wide and 12 inches deep.

19

20

Who'll buy my sweet blooming lavender?
Sixteen full branches for a penny.

21

◀ Check trellises and wires supporting
climbers before these plants develop
leaves and clothe their supports. Winter
winds, frost and snow often dislodge
supports. Redrill holes and use new
fixings and screws.

Flowers
Harden off summer bedding plants sown
earlier in the year in a greenhouse or
conservatory. They must be slowly
accustomed to outside conditions - do
not expose them to frost.

Lawns
Sow lawn seed about a week after the
soil has been levelled, firmed and
fertilizers added. Sow seeds evenly at
¼-½ cup/square yard. Stretch strings
across the area to form yard-wide squares
and in each area scatter seed evenly.
Then, rake it in lightly to the surface
soil. Select a seed mixture suitable for
the site's shadiness and likely wear.
Mixtures with finely bladed grasses
should be reserved for ornamental areas,
where wear is restricted.

Vegetables
Sow scallions ½ inch deep in drills
5-6 inches apart.

Vegetables
Sow garden peas 4 inches apart in drills
2 inches deep, and summer spinach
½-1 inch deep in drills 12 inches apart.

Nasturtiums grow well in poor, sandy soils.

Hardy annuals to sow outdoors this month, where they are to flower

❀ Common Mignonette
(*Reseda odorata*)

❀ Common Nasturtium
(*Tropaeolum majus*)

❀ Evening-scented Stock
(*Matthiola bicornis*)

❀ Love-lies-bleeding
(*Amaranthus caudatus*)

❀ Summer Adonis
(*Adonis aestivalis*)

Organic Gardening

Recycle broken wire hangers. Bend them to form a framework that can be covered with polythene bags. They are ideal for covering early plants, protecting them from frost and cold winds.

Evening-scented stocks are a popular feature in small gardens, growing happily in full sun or light shade.

Greenhouses ▲

Tomatoes sown earlier in the year and planted in a greenhouse will now be producing sideshoots. Remove these by bending and snapping them sideways.

Greenhouses ▲

Sow melons and cucumbers for growing in a greenhouse. Sow two seeds ½ inch deep in each pot, thinning them later to the strongest seedling. Place in 64°F.

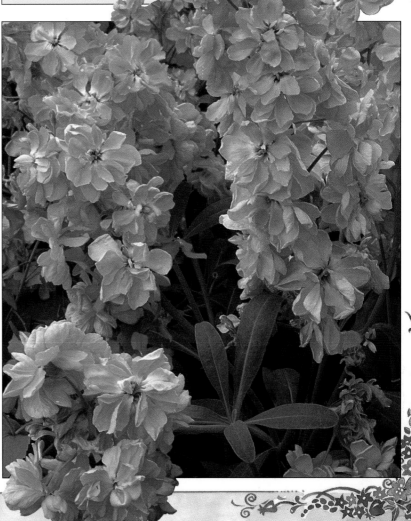

22

23

Rain, rain, go away,
Come again another day.

24

25

Rain on Good Friday or Easter Day,
A good crop of grass but a bad one of hay.

26

27

When pricking out seedlings, hold them
by their leaves - not their stems.

28

Order hanging-baskets from patio-plant
specialists to avoid disappointment
later.

Flowers ▲

Plant water lilies and other water plants.
Select the variety of water lily to suit the
depth of the pond. Put them in plastic-
mesh containers that initially can be
stood on bricks to insure they are at the
right height - leaves level with the
water's surface. As plants grow, the
bricks can be removed.

Water lilies grow well in open, sunny positions.

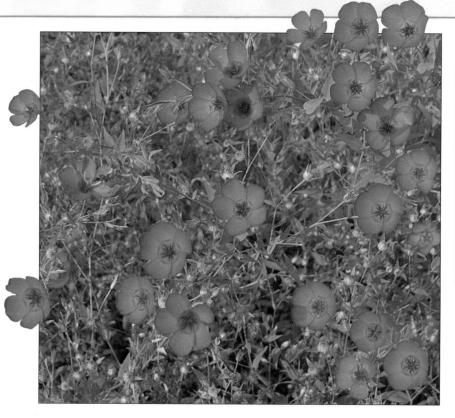

Left: Flowering flax creates a mass of saucer-shaped flowers from June through August. It is essential to sow it in full sun.

Below: A well-kept vegetable garden is a pleasure to work in. Rotating crops helps to control pests and diseases, and keeps the soil in good condition.

Lawns

Lawn seed germinates within seven to ten days of being sown. If the weather is hot and dry during this period, water the soil thoroughly but lightly so that the top few inches are moist. Just dampening the surface will do more harm than good. Covering the area with clear plastic - immediately after seeds have been sown - keeps the soil moist and warm. Keep the plastic in place with bricks or pieces of wood. Remove it when the grass seedlings are about 1 inch high.

Vegetables

Sow radishes ½ inch deep in rows 8-12 inches apart.

Vegetables

Sow maincrop potatoes 6 inches deep and 15 inches apart in rows 2½ feet apart. This insures that there is plenty of room for their development.

Organic Gardening

Plan vegetable gardens so that similar types of plants are not grown in the same place every year. Rotate crops: first potatoes; then root crops (carrots, turnips and parsnips); the following year brassicas (cabbages and Brussels sprouts); and, lastly, legumes (peas and beans). Rotating crops helps to prevent the build up of pests and diseases, as well as keeping the soil in good condition.

Greenhouses

Continue to remove sideshoots from tomato plants. Also, harden off summer-flowering plants in readiness for planting into the garden when all risk of frost has passed.

29

Mackerel sky,
Not long dry.

30

Always sow seeds thinly. Congested seedlings become weak and spindly and encourage the presence of diseases.

Above: Few sights are more impressive in a garden than a beautifully kept lawn.

Attractive and novel containers for a spring or summer display on a patio can be created from three or four car tires. Scrub the tires, stack them on top of each other and wire each one to its neighbor. Place several bricks inside, so that a large plastic bucket - with holes in its base - can be stood on them, with its rim level with the top of the tires. Paint the tires with matt-white emulsion paint. Place drainage material in the bucket's base, fill with potting compost and pack with patio-brightening plants.

A successful herbaceous border creates color and texture throughout summer.

Flowers

Keep herbaceous borders free from weeds, taking care not to damage young shoots that may be developing from established plants. When shoots are about 4 inches high, insert twiggy shoots around each clump so that stems grow up and through them. This gives support without being obtrusive.

Lawns

Feed established lawns with a quick-acting lawn fertilizer at ½ cup/square yard. Use string and canes to mark the lawn into yard-squares.

Fruit

Prune peaches and nectarines as soon as buds start to develop. Do not prune "pit" fruits in winter, when they are dormant.

Above: Sunflowers may reach 10 feet or more in height; but there are many smaller varieties.

Greenhouse

Increasingly, open the ventilators on greenhouses to prevent the temperature rising too high. Avoid drafts on plants.

Greenhouses ▲

Spring is the time when pests and diseases start to devastate plants. Check all plants thoroughly, especially under their leaves, in joints between leaf-stalks and stems, around soft shoot tips and flower buds.

Hardy annuals to sow outdoors this month, where they are to flower

- ❀ Common Sunflower
  (*Helianthus annuus*)

- ❀ Moroccan Toadflax
  (*Linaria maroccana*)

- ❀ Sweet Sultan
  (*Centaurea moschata*)

- ❀ Virginia-stock
  (*Malcolmia maritima*)

Organic Gardening ▲

Put small collars of felt around young cabbage plants to prevent cabbage root flies going down stems to attack the roots.

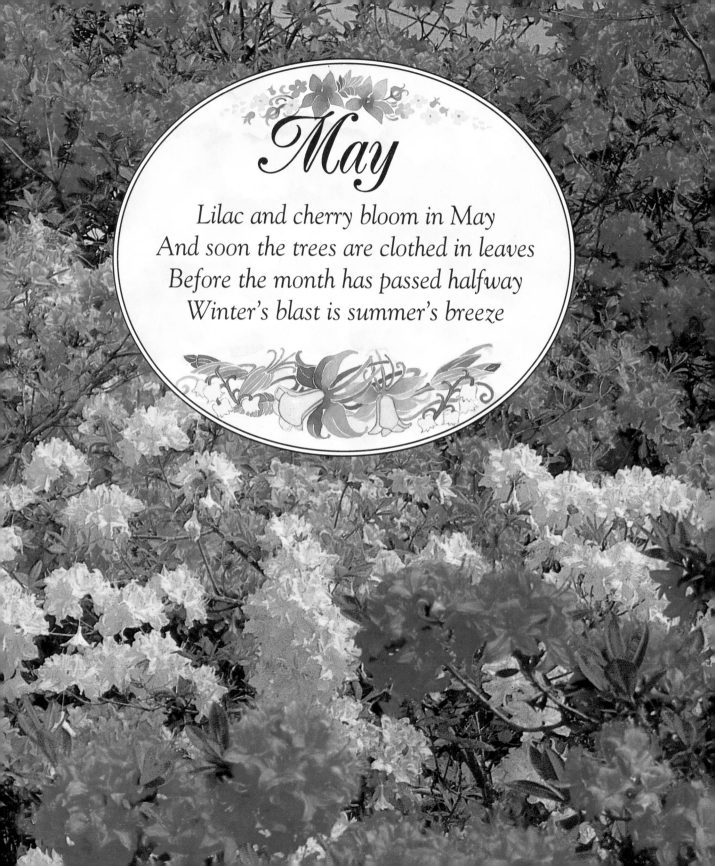

May

Lilac and cherry bloom in May
And soon the trees are clothed in leaves
Before the month has passed halfway
Winter's blast is summer's breeze

May

1

2

A swarm of bees in May is worth a load of hay.

3

4

Remove runners from strawberry plants to direct their energies into fruit production.

5

6

7

Soil at the base of walls soon becomes dry. Therefore, before planting climbers and wall shrubs in these areas, insure that the soil is moist and contains plenty of organic material, such as well-decomposed compost, that will retain moisture. It will also be necessary to water these plants regularly until their roots are established.

Flowers ▲

When filling ponds, tie a piece of cloth over the end of the hosepipe to prevent jets of water disturbing plants and soil. Alternatively, stand a bucket on bricks in the center of the pond, secure the end of a hosepipe to it and run water so that it trickles out of the bucket and into the pond.

Flowers

Thin hardy annuals sown earlier, initially to 4 inches apart, later to twice that spacing. Re-firm soil around each seedling. If left loose, roots are not in close contact with soil and will therefore become dry.

Vegetables

Sow asparagus peas 4 inches apart in drills 1 inch deep and 15-18 inches apart. When plants are a few inches high, support them with twiggy sticks.

Vegetables

Sow runner bean seeds outside in areas where the risk of frost after the third week in May is remote. If poles are to be used to support plants, put these in first. If supported by strings, these can be put up later. When supported by poles, sow two or three seeds, 2 inches deep and 4-6 inches apart, at the base of each support. If in rows and supported by strings, sow seeds 6 inches apart, 2 inches deep and in rows 2 feet apart.

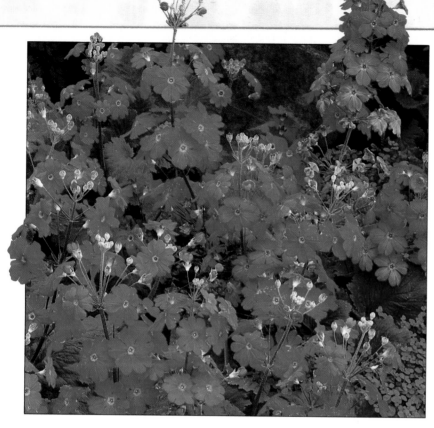

Flowers to sow this month in gentle warmth for greenhouse and home decoration

- ❀ Cineraria
  (*Senecio cruentus*)

- ❀ Fairy Primrose
  (*Primula malacoides*)

- ❀ Kew Primula
  (*Primula x kewensis*)

- ❀ Slipper Flower
  (*Calceolaria x herbeohybrida*)

Hardy annuals to sow outdoors this month where they are to flower

- ❀ Anchusa
  (*Anchusa capensis*)

- ❀ Annual Chrysanthemum
  (*Chrysanthemum carinatum*)

- ❀ Annual Mallow
  (*Lavatera trimestris*)

- ❀ Baby Blue Eyes
  (*Nemophila menziesii*)

- ❀ California Poppy
  (*Eschscholzia californica*)

- ❀ Sweet Alyssum
  (*Alyssum maritimum/Lobularia maritima*)

- ❀ Oriental Woodruff
  (*Asperula orientalis*)

Fruit

Mulch established raspberry canes with well-rotted manure or compost to keep the soil moist, cool and nourished. Also, mulch blackcurrant bushes, but first ensure that the soil is moist.

Above: The fairy primrose brings color to greenhouses and homes from December through April.

Below: Aubrietia cascades down a wall. This rock garden plant can be invasive if unchecked.

Herbaceous perennials to sow outdoors this month in a seedbed

- ❀ Anchusa
  (*Anchusa azurea*)

- ❀ Aubrietia
  (*Aubrietia deltoidea*)

- ❀ Cupid's Dart
  (*Catananche caerulea*)

- ❀ Delphinium
  (*Delphinium elatum*)

- ❀ Small Globe-Thistle
  (*Echinops ritro*)

Organic Gardening

Counteract carrot flies by masking this vegetable's attraction to pests by growing them next to onions. Alternatively, every two weeks scatter lawn-mowings between the rows.

May

8

9

When sowing seeds outdoors, mark the ends of the rows and clearly record the variety and date. Also, label seed pots and boxes.

10

11

Rambler roses will be making long shoots from their bases. Tie these to supports.

12

13

◀ If the weather becomes hot, with strong sunlight, the glass will need shading. Either paint white shading compound on the outside or use shades.

14

Flowers

Remove spring-flowering bedding plants as their flowers fade. Discard plants such as forget-me-nots and wallflowers, but carefully fork out bulbs, placing them in shallow trenches in out-of-the way places in the garden. Later, when their leaves have died down, place the bulbs in boxes and store them in a cool, airy, vermin-proof shed until late summer, when they can be replanted.

Lawns

Lawn seed sown in April soon germinates and reaches 3 inches high, when it can be cut. Use a sharp-bladed mower and cut the grass 2 inches high - no shorter. Do not use blunt mowers that tear young seedlings from the soil.

Vegetables ▲

Sow beet seeds ¾ inch deep in small clusters 5 inches apart in rows 12 inches apart. Later, thin them to one strong plant at each position.

Vegetables

Sow endive ½ inch deep in drills 15 inches apart, and radishes ½ inch deep in rows 8-12 inches apart.

Vegetables

Thin summer lettuces to 9-12 inches apart.

Above: European columbines are short-lived perennials. Plant them in well-drained soil and light shade.

Herbaceous perennials to outdoor sow this month in a seedbed

❀ European Columbine (*Aquilegia vulgaris*)

❀ New York Aster (*Aster novi-belgii*)

❀ Oregon Fleabane (*Erigeron speciosus*)

Organic Gardening

Deter flea beetles by sowing a thin line of mustard seed around the seedbed where cabbages and other brassica plants are being raised.

Below: Oregon fleabane is a colorful border plant, blooming from June through August.

Hardy annuals to sow outdoors this month where they are to flower

❀ Baby's Breath (*Gypsophila elegans*)

❀ Bachelor's Button (*Centaurea cyanus*)

❀ Clarkia (*Clarkia elegans*)

❀ Common Cosmos (*Cosmos bipinnatus*)

❀ Convolvulus (*Convolvulus tricolor/C. minor*)

❀ Flanders Field Poppy (*Papaver rhoeas*)

❀ Globe Candytuft (*Iberis umbellata*)

Greenhouse ▲

Clean the leaves of houseplants regularly. Dust and dirt are the enemies of leaves, spoiling their appearance, clogging pores and preventing sunlight reaching them. Wipe large leaves with a damp cloth, and dip smaller ones in a bowl of clean water. Do not wet the leaves when plants are in strong sunlight. Use a small, soft brush to remove dirt from hairy-leaved plants and bristly cacti.

May

15

16

Eradicate weeds from between soft fruits by shallow hoeing.

17

18

Watch out for aphids on roses. Spray as necessary.

19

20

21

◄ Indoors and in greenhouses, encourage plantlets at the ends of long stems on spider plants (*Chlorophytum comosum*) to root by pegging them into small pots of compost. Secure the plantlets with small, U-shaped pieces of wire. Sever the stems to the parent plant when they have developed roots.

Lawns
Create new lawns from turf. Such lawns can be used within a month of being laid. Thorough soil preparation is essential (see April). Lay pieces of turf in rows with their joints staggered. Brush sifted soil between the joints. If the surface is dry, use a light roller to firm them into position. During dry periods, water the entire area.

Lawns
Use selective weedkillers on established lawns when the grass is growing strongly. Do not use weedkillers if the soil is exceptionally dry or wet - and not on young lawns. Afterwards, do not cut the grass for about a week and never put the cuttings on a compost heap. Instead, burn them.

Vegetables
Carefully earth-up potato shoots, using a garden hoe to pull soil around them - but do not cover their tips.

Vegetables ▲
Mixing seeds with a gel such as wallpaper paste helps them to germinate rapidly in dry conditions. Squeeze the mixture out of a plastic bag and into a drill watered the previous day.

Fruit
If you have fruit in a wire cage or under fine-mesh netting, open up one side to allow pollinating insects to enter.

Greenhouses ▲

Continue to remove sideshoots from tomato plants. If plants are neglected at this stage, they become like a jungle and the crop is diminished.

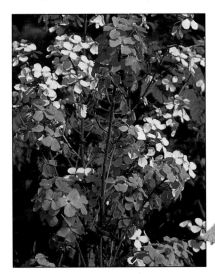

Herbaceous perennials to sow outdoors this month in a seedbed

❀ Common Yarrow
(*Achillea millefolium*)

❀ Danes' Rocket
(*Hesperis matronalis*)

❀ Fernleaf Yarrow
(*Achillea filipendula*)

❀ Red Valerian
(*Centranthus ruber*)

❀ Shasta Daisy
(*Chrysanthemum maximum*)

❀ Sneezewort
(*Achillea ptarmica*)

Left: Danes' rocket is very sweetly scented.

Below: Yarrow is superb in flower arrangements.

Hardy annuals to sow outdoors this month where they are to flower

❀ Annual Larkspur
(*Consolide ambigue*)

❀ Common Mignonette
(*Reseda odorata*)

❀ Evening-scented Stock
(*Matthiola bicornis*)

❀ Flower-of-an-hour
(*Hibiscus trionum*)

❀ Love-in-a-Mist
(*Nigella damascena*)

❀ Love-lies-bleeding
(*Amaranthus caudatus*)

❀ Nasturtium
(*Tropaeolum majus*)

Organic Gardening

Don't kill centipedes. Unlike millepedes, which chew plants, centipedes eat insect pests such as grubs, slugs and woodlice. Centipedes have one pair of legs on each body segment, whereas millepedes have two and are slow-moving.

May

22

23

Continue to sow peas, carrots, radishes and scallions.

24

25

If large gooseberry fruits are desired on dessert varieties, thin them slightly.

26

27

28

Keep grass short around fruit trees. If long, it retards the establishment of young trees.

Flowers

Plant summer-flowering bedding plants that have been thoroughly hardened off. In warm areas this job can be tackled earlier, while in extremely cold regions, where frosts may occur until the first week in June, delay planting for a week.

Flowers

Where naturalized bulbs are overcrowded, lift, divide and replant them.

Vegetables ▲

Harvest asparagus stalks when 6 inches high. Use an asparagus knife to sever them 4 inches below the surface.

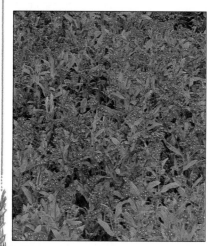

Forget-me-nots will need watering in dry weather.

Vegetables ▲

Plant leeks when about 6 inches long in holes 4-6 inches deep and 9 inches apart in rows 12-15 inches apart. Trim off long leaves and straggly roots, then drop one plant in each hole. Do not pack the hole with soil, just water each plant.

Greenhouses

Birds and cats invade greenhouses when ventilators and doors are left open. Cover ventilators with netting or wire-mesh. For doors, make a wooden framework and cover with wire-mesh.

Greenhouses

Regularly mist-spray smooth-surfaced houseplants. Avoid dampening flowers by placing small pieces of card in front of them. If flowers become wet they soon decay, encouraging other parts to deteriorate. ▼

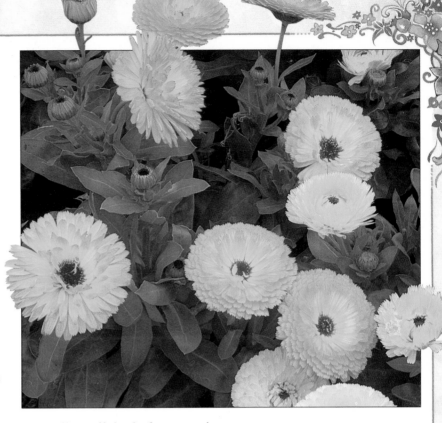

Pot marigolds, a trouble-free, free-flowering annual.

Hardy annuals to sow outdoors this month where they are to flower

- ❀ Flowering Flax
  (*Linum grandiflorum*)

- ❀ Meadow-foam
  (*Limnanthes douglasii*)

- ❀ Pincushion Plant
  (*Cotula barbata*)

- ❀ Pot Marigold
  (*Calendula officinalis*)

- ❀ Snow-on-the-Mountain
  (*Euphorbia marginata*)

- ❀ Summer Adonis
  (*Adonis aestivalis*)

Biennials to sow outdoors this month in a seedbed

- ❀ Alpine Wallflower
  (*Erysimum linifolium*)

- ❀ Canterbury Bell
  (*Campanula medium*)

- ❀ English Daisy
  (*Bellis perennis*)

- ❀ Forget-me-not
  (*Myosotis sylvatica*)

Organic gardening

Earthworms are essential to gardens, so do not kill them. They help aerate soil, improve drainage and assist in mixing dead plant and animal remains in the soil.

May

29

Cast not a clout ere May is out.

30

During dry periods, water plants thoroughly. Wall-trained trees especially suffer in dry periods.

31

Lilies create a dazzling display. Keep the soil moist and mulched.

It is still possible to sow lawn seed and to lay turf. First, however, thoroughly prepare the soil (see April)

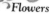

Flowers

Water and mulch lilies. Ensure the soil is moist and free from weeds before forming a mulch 2-3 inches thick.

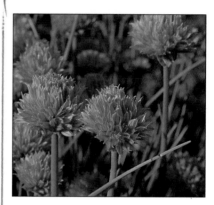

Vegetables ▲

Divide chives. Remove congested plants from their pots and pull the soil-balls gently into several pieces. Discard old central parts, repotting only pieces from around the outside.

Vegetables ▲

Keep seedlings and plants free from weeds, as they encourage the presence of pests and diseases, use soil-moisture and suffocate plants. Use an onion hoe (like a miniature garden hoe) carefully to sever weeds around seedlings. Re-firm soil around plants if it is loosened.

Fruit

Inspect fruit bushes and trees regularly to check for the presence of pests and diseases. Spray immediately, following the manufacturer's instructions.

Greenhouses

Repot plants indoors and in greenhouses that fill their pots with roots. Check that their roots are free from root pests, such as root mealy bugs (like small woodlice), and select a clean pot slightly larger than the present one. Firm potting compost gently around the root-ball, leaving a ½ inch space at the top to allow for watering.

Greenhouses

Repot chrysanthemums which will later flower in pots in greenhouses and conservatories. Stand them outdoors on a firm, well-drained surface. If plants are placed on a soft piece of ground, a heavy storm might cause them to fall over.

Honesty creates a mass of fragrant, purple flowers from April to June.

Left: Hollyhocks – familiar plants in a border.

Hardy annuals to sow outdoors this month where they are to flower

- ❀ Common Sunflower
  (Helianthus annus)

- ❀ MoroccanToadflax
  (Linaria maroccana)

- ❀ Pincushion Flower
  (Scabiosa atropurpurea)

- ❀ Stardust
  (Gilia lutea)

- ❀ Sweet Sultan
  (Centaurea moschata)

- ❀ Tassel Flower
  (Emilia flammea)

- ❀ Virginia-Stock
  (Malcolmia maritima)

Biennials to sow outdoors this month in a seedbed

- ❀ Foxglove
  (Digitalis purpurea)

- ❀ Hollyhock
  (Alcea [Althaea] rosea)

- ❀ Honesty
  (Lunaria annua)

- ❀ Siberian Wallflower
  (Erysimum asperum)

- ❀ Wallflower
  (Cheiranthus cheiri)

Organic Gardening

Hedgehogs are a gardener's friend, eating slugs, beetles, cutworms and millepedes. Bread soaked in milk is a treat for them, especially in the fall when they need to gain body weight prior to hibernation.

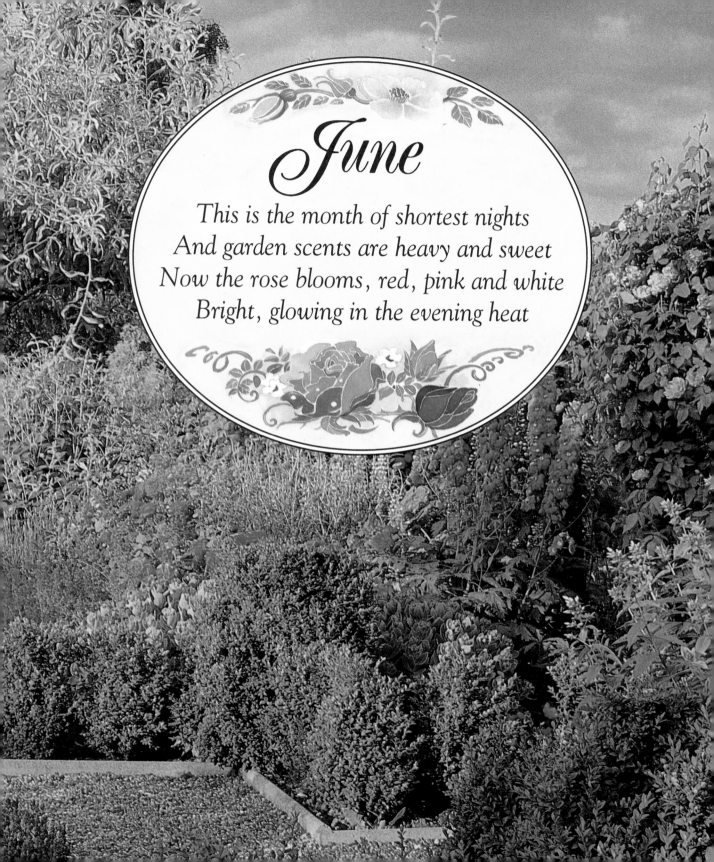

June

This is the month of shortest nights
And garden scents are heavy and sweet
Now the rose blooms, red, pink and white
Bright, glowing in the evening heat

June

1

Calm weather in June, set corn in tune.

2

3

4

5

6

Flowers
Tie up shoots of delphiniums to prevent them being damaged. Also, check other border plants to ensure they will not be damaged by wind and rain.

Lawns
When cutting grass, avoid treading on it immediately before it is cut. For safety, wear strong shoes, and keep pets and children off it while it is being mown. And do not cut it when wet. If using an electric mower, start cutting at the side nearest the power source - there is then less chance of the cord being severed. And insure a circuit-breaker is fitted into the power supply so that if the cord is cut, the electricity is instantly cut off.

Vegetables
Harvest rapid-growing salad crops such as radishes and scallions, and use the space to sow another crop that matures quickly.

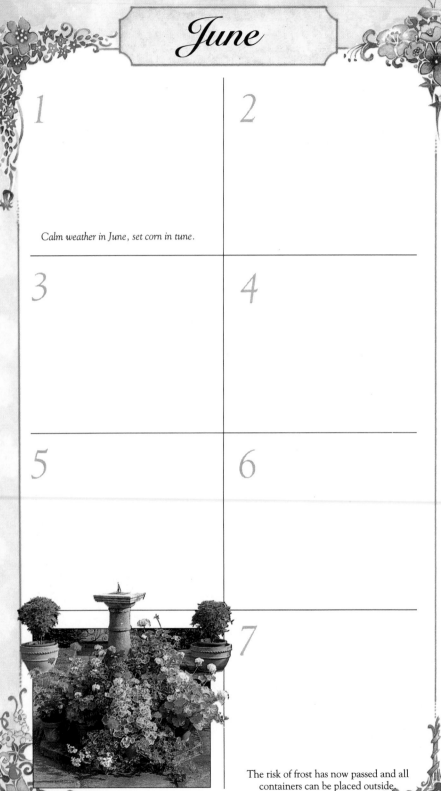

7

The risk of frost has now passed and all containers can be placed outside.

Rose 'Rosy Mantle', a climbing hybrid tea.

Greenhouses
Take cuttings of regal pelargoniums, inserting them in equal parts moist peat and sharp sand.

Organic Gardening

Trap the larvae of codling moth as they climb trunks. Wrap strips of corrugated cardboard around trunks - the larvae believe these to be safe havens in which they can overwinter. Remove and burn them in October.

Herbaceous perennials to sow outdoors this month in a seedbed

❀ Alpine Poppy
(*Papaver alpinum*)

❀ Anchusa
(*Anchusa azurea*)

❀ Cupid's Dart
(*Catananche caerulea*)

❀ Delphinium
(*Delphinium elatum*)

Flowers to sow this month in gentle warmth to produce plants for greenhouse and home decoration

❀ Cineraria
(*Senecio cruentus*)

❀ Fairy Primrose
(*Primula malacoides*)

❀ Kew Primrose
(*Primula x kewensis*)

❀ Slipper Flower
(*Calceolaria x herbeohybrida*)

Vegetables
Transplant Brussels sprouts into their growing positions, 2½ feet apart in rows 2½-3 feet apart.

Fruit
Blackberries and hybrid berries will produce new canes throughout summer.

A careful choice of garden ornaments will enhance any garden.

June

8

9

10

Pick strawberries as soon as they are ripe. If left on plants they soon deteriorate. Place the fruits in small baskets to avoid them being squashed.

11

Cut lawns regularly. The more often they are mown, the less nutrients the grass takes from the soil.

Vegetables
Pinch out the tips of fava beans to reduce the risk of black bean aphids attacking young shoots. It also encourages plants to produce pods.

Flowers
Tidy up early-flowering rock garden plants. Removing dead leaves and flowers helps to reduce the risk of attack from slugs and snails.

12

13

14

Remove dead flowers from plants growing in tubs, window-boxes, troughs and hanging-baskets. Cutting them off encourages the development of more flowers and smartens the display.

Hanging baskets and garden tubs planted with a medley of summer flowers.

Herbaceous perennials to sow outdoors this month in a seedbed

- ❀ European Columbine
  (*Aquilegia vulgaris*)
- ❀ Iceland Poppy
  (*Papaver nudicaule*)
- ❀ Oregon Fleabane
  (*Erigeron speciosus*)
- ❀ Oriental Poppy
  (*Papaver orientale*)
- ❀ Small Globe-Thistle
  (*Echinops ritro*)

Organic Gardening

Slugs devastate seedlings and other soft plants, especially when the weather is warm and wet. Slug traps are effective, but need clearing each morning. Soup-plates filled with beer and brown sugar attract these pests. Alternatively, bury wide-topped glass jars so that their rims are level with the surrounding soil. Fill with the beer mixture. Slugs fall in and drown.

Left: Small globe-thistles are easily grown.

Below: The richly colored oriental poppy.

Lawns

Feed established lawns with a quick-acting lawn fertilizer at ½ cup/square yard. Insure it is spread evenly. For large areas, wheeled fertilizer distributors speed up this job.

Greenhouses

Do not neglect to water plants. Once the compost is dry - especially if a peat-based type - it is difficult to make it again uniformly moist. At the height of summer, water plants in the morning and again during the late afternoon.

Greenhouses

Damp down greenhouses to create a moist atmosphere by mist-spraying the plants, floor and staging. Do this in early morning or by mid-afternoon, so that excess moisture disappears by nightfall. A moist atmosphere at night, when the temperature falls, encourages the presence of diseases.

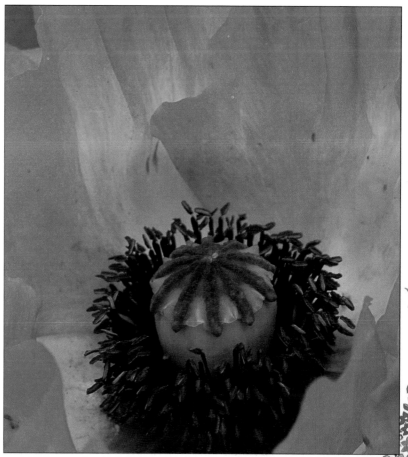

June

15

Continue to tie new raspberry canes to supporting wires. Allow only eight canes to develop from each plant.

16

17

18

Water and feed tomato plants regularly, every two weeks.

19

20

21

Summer-prune gooseberries by shortening sideshoots to five leaves. This directs their vigor into the development of fruit buds.

Flowers
Water hanging-baskets regularly as the compost dries out rapidly, especially when positioned in strong sunlight. Tie the end of a hosepipe to a short cane. Water can then be dribbled into the basket without the need to stand on a stool.

Above: Marjoram, a well-known culinary herb.

Flowers

Keep soil moist during dry periods. It is better to apply water gently over several hours than to swamp the surface in a few moments. Too much water at one time destroys the soil's structure and it just runs off the surface without penetrating to the roots. Also, apply water during evenings, not in the day when much of it would rapidly evaporate.

Flowers

Regularly check plants to insure they are not infested with pests or diseases. At this time of year plants are quickly devastated by pests.

Flowers

Rotary grass cutters, such as strimmers, help to cut weeds and long grass under shrubs - without having to bend down.

Vegetables

Lift early potatoes. Avoid damaging the tubers - dig under them with a fork, preferably a broad-tined type. Remove soil, wash the tubers and allow to dry.

Greenhouses

Perpetual-flowering carnations are often infested by red spider mites at this time of year. In addition to spraying with pesticides, regularly mist-spray the plants. Greenfly are another pest that attacks carnations, especially around the soft tips of shoots and flower buds.

Greenhouses

Take cuttings of marjoram. Water plants before taking cuttings, each 2-3 inches long. Remove the lower leaves and insert them in sandy compost. Water the compost to settle it around the roots and place the pot on a lightly shaded shelf, either indoors or in a greenhouse.

Organic Gardening

Instead of using garden compost as a mulch around plants, newspapers can be used. Spread four to six thicknesses of newspaper over the soil, weighing it down with stones.

Herbaceous perennials to sow outdoors this month in a seedbed

❀ Common Yarrow
(Achillea millefolium)

❀ Danes' Rocket
(Hesperis matronalis)

❀ Fernleaf Yarrow
(Achillea filipendula)

❀ Red Valerian
(Centranthus ruber)

❀ Shasta Daisy
(Chrysanthemum maximum)

June

22

Plant *orange-eye butterfly bush*, thymes and ▷
New York asters to attract butterflies.

23

24

25

Summer-prune both red and white
currants, shortening lateral shoots to five
leaves - but do not cut the leader shoots.

26

27

Immature fruits frequently fall from apple
trees this month. This is quite normal and
is the tree's way of ridding itself of excess
fruits.

28

❧ The best lavender to use for hedging is
"Hidcote".

Flowers ❧
Divide congested flag irises as soon as
their flowers fade. Lift and divide
clumps, discarding the old, central part
and replanting younger parts from
around the outside. A sharp knife is
usually necessary for this job.

Flowers
Remove sucker shoots from the bases of
roses. Do not cut them off at soil-level.
Instead, remove soil from around the
sucker, and sever close to its base.

Lawns

By this month, bare patches appear in lawns. Loosen the surface with a fork, gently re-firm and scatter lawn seed at ½ cup/square yard. Water lightly and cover with clear plastic until the seedlings are about 1 inch high.

Vegetables

Lettuce can still be sown - until late July. Sow seed ½ inch deep in drills 12-15 inches apart. Radishes can also be sown now.

Greenhouses

Whitefly often infests tomato plants and cinerarias. Spray or fumigate these plants, repeating the treatment ten days later to kill young whitefly that have hatched since the first treatment.

Greenhouses

Large houseplants that fill their pots with roots cannot easily be repotted. Instead, gently scrape away the surface compost and replace with a fresh potting mixture, leaving space at the top so that the plant can be watered.

Above: The gloriously colored Iris 'Brannigan' creates a splendid display in early summer.

Right: Foxgloves thrive in partial shade.

Biennials to sow outdoors this month in a seedbed

- ❀ Alpine Wallflower
  (*Erysimum linifolium*)

- ❀ Canterbury Bell
  (*Campanula medium*)

- ❀ English Daisy
  (*Bellis perennis*)

- ❀ Forget-me-not
  (*Myosotis sylvatica*)

- ❀ Foxglove
  (*Digitalis purpurea*)

- ❀ Hollyhock
  (*Alcea [Althaea] rosea*)

- ❀ Honesty
  (*Lunaria annua*)

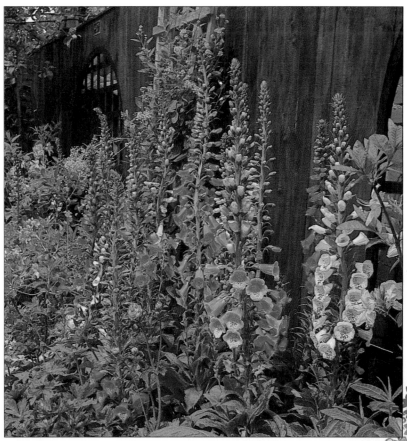

June

29

When cutting roses for flower arrangements use sharp pruning shears and sever stems just above a leaf-joint.

Rosa mundi.

30

Regularly nip out the tips of shoots on houseplants grown for their foliage to encourage them to become bushy.

Flowers
Increase cacti from cuttings. Sever stems at their bases, allow the cuts to dry for a couple of days and then insert into compost.

Flowers
Water plants in containers regularly, especially those in hanging baskets.

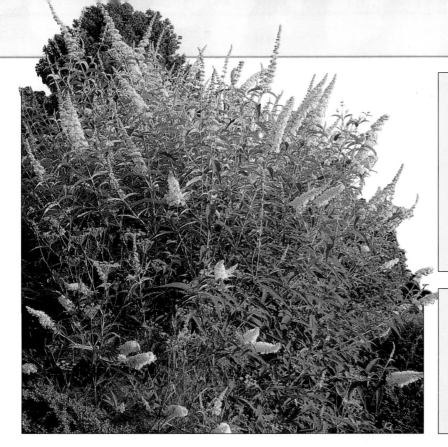

Biennials to sow outdoors this month in a seedbed

❀ Pansy
  (*Viola x wittrockiana*)

❀ Siberian Wallflower
  (*Erysimum asperum*)

❀ Sweet William
  (*Dianthus barbatus*)

❀ Wallflower
  (*Cheiranthus cheiri*)

Organic Gardening

In summer there are many plants that attract clouds of butterflies. These include buddleias, marigolds, *Helichrysum bracteatum*, lobelia, mignonette, scabious, Sweet Williams, lilac and thyme.

Above: Buddleia davidii *"White Cloud"*

Below: Lobelia, a perfect edging plant.

Lawns
Cut lawns regularly. If grass is allowed to become high, cutting is difficult and after mowing may leave yellow patches that take many weeks to regain a rich green color. If the weather is very hot, do not cut the grass short.

Vegetables
Support peas with pea-sticks or wire-netting. Keep the plants well watered, especially when the pods start to form.

Fruit
Keep grass short in orchards, especially around young fruit trees. The grass deprives plants of nitrogen, an essential growth-promoting fertilizer for young trees.

Greenhouses
Flowers soon fall off plants in pots when the compost is allowed to become dry. Check regularly that the compost is moist - but not waterlogged.

July

A summer breeze feels like a sigh
And summer's days are long and warm
Almost every garden in July
Is rich with color, scent and form

July

1

2

A full moon brings fair weather.

3

4

Regularly hoe between crops to eradicate weeds.

Flowers ▲
Prune shrubs that have finished flowering, such as weigelas, deutzias and mock orange, to encourage the development of young shoots that will bear flowers during the following year. If these shrubs are neglected, they become a tangled mass of stems bearing inferior flowers.

5

6

Feed rose bushes to encourage a further flush of flowers.

7

Many herbaceous plants do not need staking and are ideal for planting in borders totally surrounded by grass. They are known as "island beds." Three kidney-shaped island beds with paths between them create a superb feature during summer. On a smaller scale, a single border in the corner of a serpentine-edged lawn is attractive.

Flowers
Remove dead flowers to encourage plants to produce more blooms. This is especially important for plants growing in containers.

Hedges
Trim hedges regularly, especially privet. If left unclipped, they become untidy and eventually bare of shoots and leaves at their bases. ▼

Lawns
Repair the edges of lawns. Cut out a section of grass, 8-10 inches wide and 15-18 inches long. Undercut this strip and reverse it so that the broken part is towards the lawn's center. Fill up the damaged area with friable soil, firm and sow with lawn seed.

Vegetables
Transplant winter cabbages from their seedbed to cropping positions, setting them 18-24 inches apart each way.

Vegetables
Thin beets, carrots and lettuces. Congested plants never produce good crops.

Fruit
Protect fruits from birds by spreading nets over them, supported on metal or wooden stakes. Preferably, construct a wire fruit cage that will protect bushes and trees throughout the year.

Greenhouses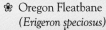
Increase large-leafed begonias such as *Begonia rex* from leaf-cuttings. Cut the veins on the lower side and lay the leaf on moist compost, securing it in place with bent wires or small stones.

Left: A magnificent late-summer herbaceous border packed with yellow crocosmia, pink geraniums, golden marguerites and purple cone flowers.

Right: Begonia rex, *a superb houseplant.*

Flowers to sow this month in gentle warmth to produce plants for greenhouse and home decoration

❀ Cineraria
  (*Senecio cruentus*)

❀ Fairy Primrose
  (*Primula malacoides*)

❀ Kew Primrose
  (*Primula x kewensis*)

❀ Slipper Flower
  (*Calceolaria x herbeohybrida*)

Herbaceous perennials to sow outdoors this month in a seedbed

❀ Alpine Poppy
  (*Papaver alpinum*)

❀ Candle Larkspur
  (*Delphinium elatum*)

❀ Iceland Poppy
  (*Papaver nudicaule*)

❀ Oregon Fleatbane
  (*Erigeron speciosus*)

July

8

Cut lettuces as they mature. For "hearted" types press each lettuce's top and if firm, it is ready to be cut. Use a sharp knife.

9

10

11

A swarm of bees in July is not worth a fly.

12

13

Cut cauliflowers when curds are mature.

14

Dogs often dig holes in lawns. Repair these by placing a piece of board, 12-15 inches square, over the hole. Use an edging-iron or spade to cut around the board, then remove the damaged turf. From an out-of-the-way area, cut a similar-sized turf and place in the hole. Firm it in place, trickle friable soil into cracks and water thoroughly.

Flowers ▲
Increase garden pinks by taking 3 inch long cuttings and inserting them in small pots of sandy compost. Place them in a cold frame or cool greenhouse.

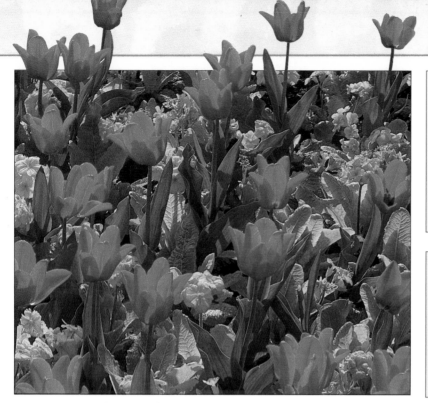

Herbaceous perennials to sow outdoors this month in a seedbed

❀ Mullein
   (*Verbascum phoeniceum*)

❀ Oriental Poppy
   (*Papaver orientale*)

❀ Tickseed
   (*Coreopsis grandiflora*)

Organic Gardening

Chalcid wasps attack moths, butterflies and scale insects. One form is *Encarsia formosa*, which is especially effective at controlling greenhouse whitefly. It lays its eggs in the scale-like nymphs, which later turn black.

Above: A fine group of tulips and polyanthus.

Below: Dianthus 'Whatfield Ruby'

Flowers
Tulips heeled-in when the ground was needed for summer bedding plants can be lifted, cleaned and placed in a cool, dark, dry and vermin-proof place until replanted in the fall.

Lawns
Grass beneath children's swings soon wears out in summer - but do not replace it with concrete. Instead, either re-turf the area or place a large rubber mat under the swing.

Vegetables
Water runner beans regularly during dry periods. Mulching the soil around them with a 3-inch thick layer helps to retain moisture around their roots. But first, water the soil thoroughly.

Fruit
Plant new strawberry plants from now through mid-August, as well as in early spring. Buy plants certified free from disease. Plant them 15-18 inches apart in rows 2½ feet apart. Firm soil around them and water thoroughly.

Greenhouses
Do not allow coleus plants to flower. Pick them off as soon as they appear. This plant is grown for its attractive leaves.

July

15

Water both French beans and runner beans in dry seasons.

16

17

18

Feed air-plants by misting them with a weak - about a quarter of the normal strength - liquid fertilizer once a month from spring through late summer.

19

20

Bend leaves over cauliflower curds to protect them from strong sunlight.

21

Weeds

Keep borders free from weeds by using a hoe. Ensure the roots of perennial weeds are removed, as well as their leaves and stems. If left unchecked, weeds suffocate plants, rob the soil of plant foods and encourage the presence of pests and diseases.

Flowers

Late-flowering chrysanthemums in pots that have been placed outdoors will need to have their canes tied to horizontal wires to prevent them being blown over.

Lawns

Ants can be a nuisance on lawns, although usually they do little harm. However, they remove soil from around roots, which in dry weather distresses the grass. Ant repellants can be used, but ensure they are suitable for lawns.

Vegetables ▲

Harvest globe artichokes when their scales are still tight. The heads at the tops of plants mature first, those on lateral shoots slightly later.

Vegetables

Harvest shallots. Insert a garden fork under them gently to loosen the soil.

Greenhouses

Pick cucumbers regularly to encourage the development of further fruits.

Greenhouses

Pot on plants as they fill their pots with roots.

Left: Chrysanthemum 'Deane Joy'

Biennials to sow this month

❀ Forget-me-not
   (*Myosotis sylvatica*)

❀ Pansy
   (*Viola x wittrockiana*)

Organic Gardening

Water is becoming increasingly scarce, water companies frequently banning its use in gardens. Install butts to collect from water rain gutters.

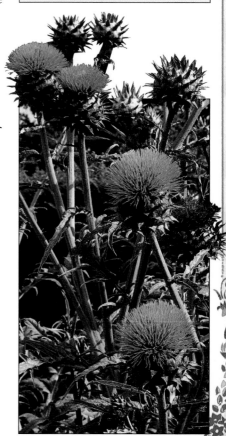

Above: Cardoons have eye-catching flowers.

July

22

23

Water soft or hairy-leaved houseplants that have become very dry by standing them in bowls containing a little water. When moisture reaches the surface, remove the pot and allow excess water to drain.

24

Trim back sage that has flowered lightly.

25

26

27

Water urn plants by filling their centers with water. They can also be fed in this way, with a quarter-strength feed every three or four weeks from spring to late summer.

28

Blanch chicory by loosely tying its stems together with raffia.

Flowers
Feed dahlia plants, hoeing and watering it into the soil. After thoroughly soaking the soil, form a 3-inch thick mulch around them to conserve moisture.

Flowers
Plant colchicum as soon as they can be bought, setting the corms 3-4 inches deep and in small clusters.

Flowers
Remove faded flower heads from large-flowered rhododendrons. Snap the old flower head sideways.

Vegetables
Sow turnips and rutabagas thinly in drills ¾ inch deep and in rows 15 inches apart. Ensure that the soil is moist.

Below: A beautifully planted urn. Be sure to keep urns and tubs well watered during hot weather. They often need watering twice a day.

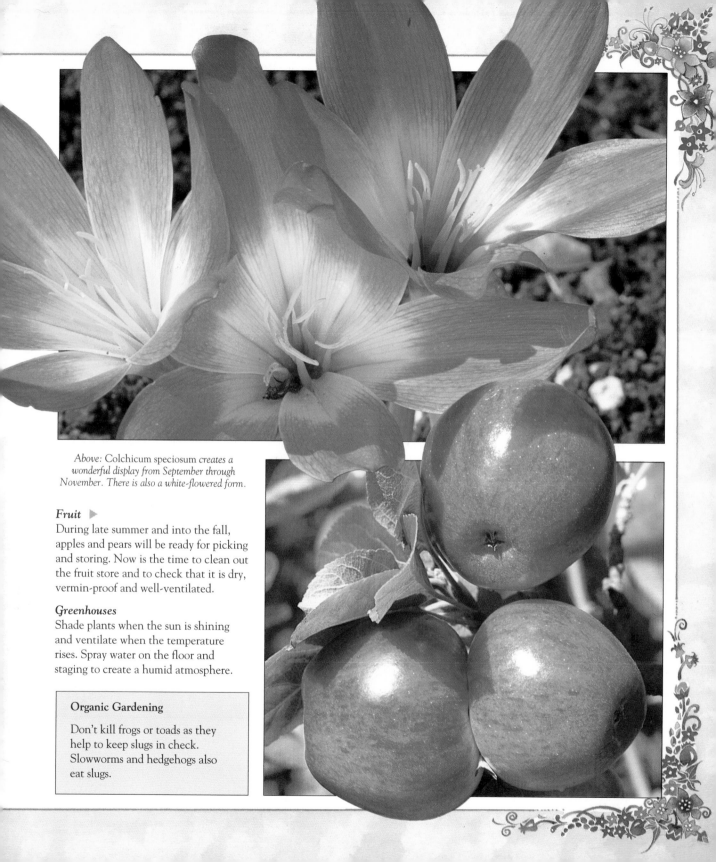

Above: Colchicum speciosum *creates a wonderful display from September through November. There is also a white-flowered form.*

Fruit ▷

During late summer and into the fall, apples and pears will be ready for picking and storing. Now is the time to clean out the fruit store and to check that it is dry, vermin-proof and well-ventilated.

Greenhouses

Shade plants when the sun is shining and ventilate when the temperature rises. Spray water on the floor and staging to create a humid atmosphere.

Organic Gardening

Don't kill frogs or toads as they help to keep slugs in check. Slowworms and hedgehogs also eat slugs.

July

29

30

31

Flowers

Transplant wallflowers, sweet williams and Canterbury bells into a nursery bed to give them more space, in readiness for planting into their flowering positions in the fall. To ensure the plants transplant successfully, water both the seedlings and the nursery bed the day before they are moved.

Pinch out the growing points of dwarf beans to keep them compact.

Most houseplants like a humid atmosphere around their leaves. When displaying plants individually, moisture given off by leaves soon disperses, but when plants are in groups they create humid micro-climates.

Flowers

Disbud chrysanthemums that are not being grown as spray types. Leave the terminal buds but remove the small ones around them by bending them sideways.

Right: Chrysanthemum 'Rystar', a summer-flowering type that does not need to be disbudded. It is ideal for planting in borders in a garden.

Above: Houseplants arranged in a group create a humid micro-climate around themselves. This is especially beneficial during hot summers.

Flowers

Increase shrubs such as escallonias, weigelas and deutzias by taking half-ripe cuttings. Insert them in equal parts moist peat and sharp sand.

Vegetables

When outdoor tomato plants have formed four trusses, pinch out the plant's growing tip. Snap this off sideways, slightly above the second leaf above the fourth truss.

Vegetables

Earth up celery grown in trenches. First, tie the stems together to prevent soil getting into their centers.

Fruit

Tidy up strawberry beds by removing old leaves and cutting off runners.
Hoe lightly between the plants.

Fruit

Increase blackberries by layering long shoots, pegging them into the soil and tying the tip to a small stake.

Organic Gardening

Green manuring helps to improve a soil's fertility and to prevent the growth of weeds. Crops such as red clover, lucerne and annual lupins are sown and later dug into the soil.

Above: Weigela florida 'Variegata'

August

Long afternoons in hot August
Come to thunder by and by
But then, soon after a cloudburst
The sun returns to warm and dry

August

1

Harvest globe artichokes when their scales are still tight.

2

3

4

Feed lawns with a slow-acting lawn fertilizer.

5

6

Gather herbs for drying.

7

◀ Pick beans while young and tender. This encourages the development of further pods.

Flowers
Pick sweet pea flowers regularly to encourage the development of further blooms.

Vegetables
Sow spring cabbages in seedbeds, in drills ¾ inch deep and 6-8 inches apart. Later, move the young plants to a vegetable plot.

Vegetables
Lift second-early and maincrop potatoes after their leaves and stems have died down.

Fruit ▲
Trees heavily laden with fruit may need to have their branches supported, either with strings from a central pole or with wooden props.

Greenhouses
Remove lower leaves from tomato plants to improve air circulation and enable more light to reach the fruits.

Organic Gardening

Ichneumon flies lay eggs in some caterpillar pests, which later hatch and devour them. Take care not to kill these insects.

Greenhouses
Increase dumb canes (*Dieffenbachia*) by cutting thick stems into pieces about 3 inches long, each containing at least one bud. Lay each piece on the surface of equal parts moist peat and sharp sand, and secure with pieces of bent wire. Cover with a domed plastic lid or plastic bag until shoots appear, then pot up individually.

Greenhouses
Pick tomatoes regularly to encourage the development of further fruits.

Below: Dumb canes, tender plants for homes and greenhouses, have large, colorful leaves.

Above: Pick sweet peas regularly to encourage the development of more blooms. They are superb in gardens, as well as in flower arrangements.

Flowers to sow this month in gentle warmth to produce plants for greenhouse and home decoration

❀ Cineraria
(*Senecio cruentus*)

❀ Fairy Primrose
(*Primula malacoides*)

August

8

9

Pick cucumbers as they mature.

10

11

Remove sideshoots from tomato plants.

12

13

Continue to cut lawns regularly, as well as trimming the edges.

14

Plant bulbs of imperial fritillarias 8 inches deep, from now until October.

Flowers

Cordon-grown sweet peas which have reached the tops of their supports can be untied, lowered, stems trailed along the ground and trained up supports further down the row.

Flowers ▷

Before going on vacation, insure arrangements have been made to water your houseplants. Place plants in bowls containing a little water, or on expanded clay particles in trays of water. Alternatively, trail the end of a capillary mat in a sink of water, the other end draped over a draining board. Plants stood on top will slowly absorb moisture by capillary action.

Vegetables

Sow turnips and rutabagas thinly in drills ½ inch deep and 12 inches apart. First water the drills.

Below: Imperial fritillarias have impressive flowers in April. Their bulbs can be planted now.

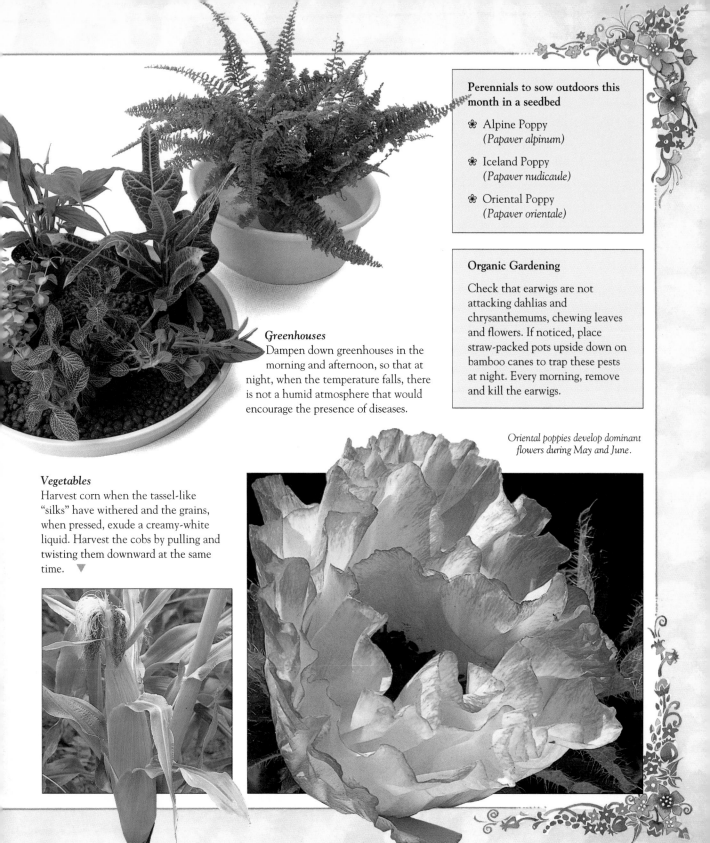

Perennials to sow outdoors this month in a seedbed

❀ Alpine Poppy
(*Papaver alpinum*)

❀ Iceland Poppy
(*Papaver nudicaule*)

❀ Oriental Poppy
(*Papaver orientale*)

Organic Gardening

Check that earwigs are not attacking dahlias and chrysanthemums, chewing leaves and flowers. If noticed, place straw-packed pots upside down on bamboo canes to trap these pests at night. Every morning, remove and kill the earwigs.

Greenhouses
Dampen down greenhouses in the morning and afternoon, so that at night, when the temperature falls, there is not a humid atmosphere that would encourage the presence of diseases.

Oriental poppies develop dominant flowers during May and June.

Vegetables
Harvest corn when the tassel-like "silks" have withered and the grains, when pressed, exude a creamy-white liquid. Harvest the cobs by pulling and twisting them downward at the same time. ▼

August

15

16

17

18

Hoe lightly between rows of newly planted strawberries, severing weeds and creating friable soil.

19

20

21

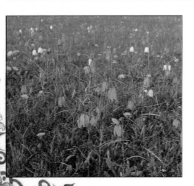

Don't dig up plants growing wild in fields for transplanting into your garden. It is illegal. Moreover, the seeds of many of them are available from seed companies.

Lawns
Earthworms are beneficial in gardens, but in lawns they can be a problem by producing casts on the surface. These can be brushed or raked off, but if the surface becomes a mess, worms can be deterred by the use of a proprietary worm deterrent.

Vegetables
Pick fava beans before the pods become tough. Also, harvest garden peas while young and tender.

Fruit
Pick apples as soon as they are ready. Cup your hand around the base of each fruit and lift gently, twisting and tilting your hand at the same time. If the stalk remains on the fruit but parts from the spur, it is ready to be picked. Treat each fruit gently as if bruised, it soon deteriorates when stored.

Greenhouses
Mist-spray aerial roots on houseplants such as the Swiss cheese plant (*Monstera deliciosa*) and philodendrons. This prevents them becoming dry and hard. ▼

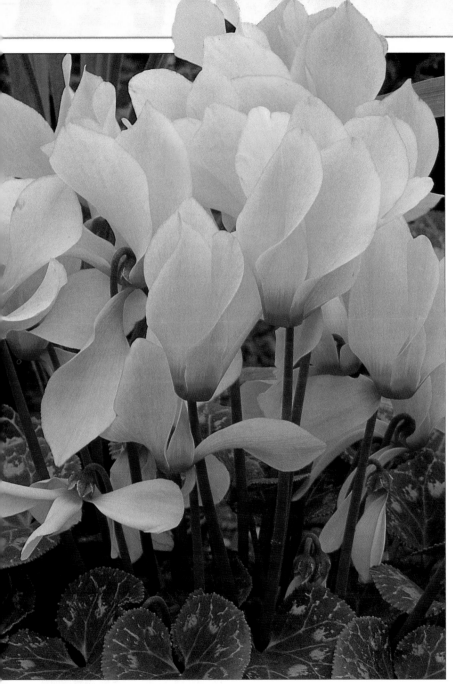

Annuals suitable for growing as cut-flowers for room decoration

❀ African Daisy
   (*Arctotis grandis*)

❀ Annual Chrysanthemum
   (*Chrysanthemum carinatum*)

❀ Baby's Breath
   (*Gypsophila elegans*)

❀ China Aster
   (*Callistephus chinensis*)

❀ Clarkia
   (*Clarkia elegans*)

❀ Coneflower
   (*Rudbeckia hirta*)

❀ Common Cosmos
   (*Cosmos bipinnatus*)

Organic Gardening

Rove beetles live in the soil and eat mites and the pupae of cabbage root flies. Both the adults and larvae of these beetles are beneficial to gardeners, and should not be destroyed.

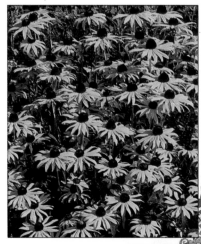

Greenhouses

Re-pot the previous year's cyclamen that were left in their pots and placed on their sides in a greenhouse after flowering. Remove the corm and repot into fresh compost.

Above: Cyclamen persicum is sold in hundreds of thousands during December. Always place them in cool rooms, away from heat and direct sun.

Right: Rudbeckia sullivantii "Goldstrum" is a perennial coneflower which flowers from July through September.

August

22

23

Blanch cardoons. First, wrap black plastic around them.

24

25

Harvest scallions while young.

26

27

Hoe regularly between plants. ▶

28

Lift beets, using a garden fork to ease them from the soil.

Flowers
Increase the maternity plant (*Kalanchoe daigremontiana*) and the *Kalanchoe tubiflora* by removing the young plantlets that grow on their leaves and pressing them into moist compost. When rooted, pot them up into small pots.

Flowers
Attractive indoor features can be created by securing small bromeliads to a branch, about 3-3¼ feet long, fixed vertically in a large pot or small tub. Mist-spray plants regularly, especially during their establishment.

Vegetables
The acidity or alkalinity of soil can be assessed by using a simple soil-testing kit. Mix a random sample of soil with chemicals, creating a color that when compared with a color chart indicates the soil's pH. The degree of acidity shows the amount of lime needed. Never use lime at the same time as applying manure or compost. Indeed, it is best to dig soil and incorporate organic material, then later to apply lime.

*Above: Nemesia, one of the jewels in a garden,
forms a fine display from June through August.*

*Right: Godetias are hardy annuals with flowers
from June through August.*

Organic Gardening

It is surprising how much money
can be saved each year by
recycling supporting wires, canes,
poles, boxes and string. As crops
are harvested or die, clean their
supports and store in a shed.

Fruit
Blackcurrants planted the previous the
fall or early in the year will have
developed young shoots from their bases.
Cut out at soil-level the weakest of
these. Shoots that are left will produce
fruit during the following year.

Greenhouses ▷
When growing houseplants with aerial
roots, provide them with a moss-covered
pole so that moisture is retained to keep
them soft and pliable.

Annuals suitable for growing as cut-flowers for room decoration

❀ Common Mignonette
  (*Reseda odorata*)

❀ Godetia
  (*Godetia grandiflora*)

❀ Herb Tree-mallow
  (*Lavatera trimestris*)

❀ Love-in-a-Mist
  (*Nigella damascena*)

❀ Love-lies-bleeding
  (*Amaranthus caudatus*)

❀ Nasturtium
  (*Tropaeolum majus*)

❀ Nemesia
  (*Nemesia strumosa*)

August

29

30

31

Bend over the tops of onions in preparation for lifting them.

Flowers

Disbud chrysanthemums that are not being grown as spray varieties. Leave the terminal bud and remove the small buds from around it gently. Bend them sideways.

Vegetables

Harvest kohlrabi when the size of tennis balls.

Vegetables

Harvest runner beans while they are young and tender. If left, they become tough and stringy.

Fruit

In dry seasons it is necessary to water soft-fruit bushes and plants, especially newly planted strawberries. Insure that the soil is thoroughly soaked, not just the surface lightly moistened.

Greenhouses

Check that greenhouse shading, earlier painted on the glass, has not been washed off. Direct sunlight at this time can be too strong for many plants.

Below: African violets can be easily propagated by inserting leaf-cuttings in moist peat and sharp sand. Insert them in hormone rooting powder.

Increase African violets by cutting off a few healthy leaves, complete with their stems (petioles). Dip the ends of their short stems in a hormone rooting powder and insert three in a 3-inch wide pot containing equal parts moist peat and sharp sand. Do not position them nearer than ½ inch to the pot's edge, as if watering is neglected this is where the compost first becomes dry. When rooted, pot up individually into small pots of peat-based compost.

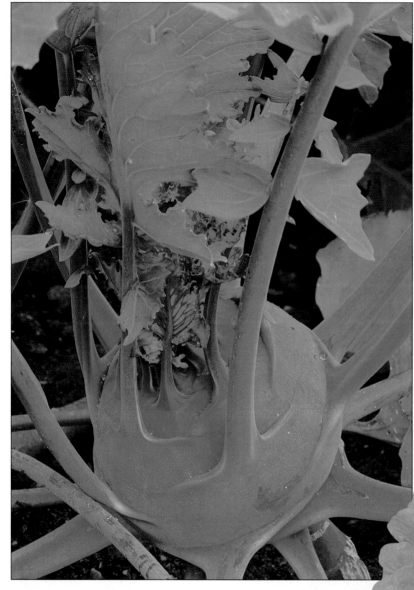

Annuals suitable for growing as cut-flowers for room decoration

❀ Moroccan Toadflax
(*Linaria maroccana*)

❀ Pot Marigold
(*Calendula officinalis*)

❀ Scabious
(*Scabiosa atropurpurea*)

❀ Sunflower
(*Helianthus annuus*)

❀ Tassel Flower
(*Emilia flammea*)

❀ Tickseed
(*Coreopsis calliopsis*)

❀ Water Cape-marigold
(*Dimorphotheca aurantica*)

❀ Zinnia
(*Zinnia elegans*)

Left: Kohlrabi will be ready to harvest this month, when the size of tennis balls.

Below: Zinnias are superb in flower arrangements, as well as in borders.

Greenhouses

Increase the jade plant (*Crassula argentea*) by pulling off a few leaves, allowing the surfaces to dry for a few days and then inserting them in equal parts moist peat and sharp sand. Position them out of direct sunlight. When rooted, pot up the leaves individually.

Organic Gardening

Ground beetles, such as the violet ground beetle, live in the soil, eating soft-tissued grubs and adult pests, including slugs and cabbage rootfly eggs. Therefore, do not kill them.

September

September fruits are on the bough
And the bright apple is king of all
Red, golden, russet - brimming now
Ripe for the picking before they fall

September

1

2

September blow soft,
Till the fruit's in the loft.

3

4

Sow winter lettuces and winter spinach.

5

6

Harvest potatoes on ground where
wireworms are troublesome.

7

Pull up dead summer-bedding plants in
preparation for planting spring-flowering
bulbs. Fork the soil and add a light
dressing of bonemeal.

Flowers ▲
Lift gladioli plants that have flowered.
Push a garden fork gently under the
plants, and lift the corms complete with
their stems. If the stems have withered
they can be easily removed from the
corms. If not, tie up the stems and hang
in a cool, airy shed until the foliage dies.

Flowers
Prune rambler roses. Untie them from
their supports, lay them on the ground
and cut out at ground-level all stems that
have borne flowers. Retain shoots made
during the current season, and tie them
to the supports.

Fruit
Continue to pick apples, as soon as their
stalks part easily from the fruiting spurs.
Each stalk must remain attached to its
fruit. Also, pick pears as soon as their
stalks readily part from the spurs.

Fruit
Cut out at soil-level raspberry canes that
bore fruit earlier in the year. Space out
the young canes, and tie them to their
supports.

Greenhouses
Continue to train shoots of the pink
jasmine (*Jasminum polyanthum*) around a
hoop, taking care not to kink the stems.
It flowers in greenhouses and indoors
from November through April, bearing
scented, white and pale pink flowers.

Greenhouses ▲
Prick out cyclamen seedlings that have developed from seeds sown in August.

Herbaceous perennials for growing as cut-flowers for room decoration

- ❀ Baby's Breath
  (*Gypsophila paniculata*)

- ❀ Bear's Breech
  (*Acanthus mollis*)

- ❀ Day Lily
  (*Hemerocallis*)

- ❀ Delphinium
  (*Delphinium elatum*)

- ❀ Italian Aster
  (*Aster amellus*)

- ❀ Painted Gaillardia
  (*Gaillardia aristata*)

Above: Italian asters *produce a colorful display.*

Left: Day lilies flower mainly from June through August, and often into early September.

Organic Gardening

Crane-fly and chafer grubs are frequently a problem on lawns in late summer and the fall. To check their presence, one evening place a damp sack over part of the lawn. Grubs that are present will be seen under the sack in the morning - remove and destroy them. If the infestation is severe, water the lawn and place a large piece of black plastic over the area. In the morning, remove and pick off the grubs.

September

8

Trim off the largest leaves from parsley to encourage the growth of fresh ones.

9

10

11

Use ground limestone when liming soil in the fall and winter - order it now.

12

13

Place cloches over outdoor tomato plants to help ripen the last fruits. First, cut the plants from their supports and lay them in a row.

14

Flowers
Cut down herbaceous plants that have flowered and look a mess. However, in cold areas leave this job until early spring. The stems provide some protection for the roots of delicate plants. Additionally, these stems look very attractive in winter when covered with frost.

Flowers
As soon as daffodil bulbs can be bought, plant them in holes about 5 inches deep. In flower beds use a trowel, but if naturalized in grass, a bulb-planting tool that removes a core of grass and soil is better. Place a bulb in each hole, and replace the turf.

Herbaceous perennials for growing as cut-flowers for room decoration

❊ Giant Desert-candle
   (*Eremurus robustus*)

❊ Globeflower
   (*Trollium x hybridus*)

❊ Goldenrod
   (*Solidago*)

❊ Great Bellflower
   (*Campanula latifolia*)

❊ Oregon Fleabane
   (*Erigeron speciosus*)

❊ Small Globe-Thistle
   (*Echinops humilis*)

Left: The spectacular giant desert-candle, which grows over head-height, needs sun and protection from cold winds. Divide clumps in the fall.

Below: Mother-in-law's tongue is a spectacular plant for the home and greenhouse. It is ideal for positioning on sunny windowsills.

Vegetables
Plant spring cabbages 10-12 inches apart in rows 12 inches apart. A few weeks later, draw a little soil around their bases to give protection from frost.

Greenhouses
Complete the harvesting of melons and clear away the plants.

Greenhouses ▷
Divide a congested mother-in-law's tongue (*Sansevieria trifasciata*). Remove carefully the pot and pull the soil-ball and roots apart gently to form several plants. Repot each part in a fresh pot and compost.

September

15

16

Don't re-use potting or seed compost - the nutrients will have been exhausted and it may contain pests and diseases.

Flowers ▲
Cut off seed-heads from honesty (*Lunaria annua*), Chinese lanterns (*Physalis alkekengi*) and poppies for decoration indoors in winter.

17

18

Tie up the leaves of chicory and place a large pot over them to blanch their stems. Block off the hole in the pot's top to exclude all light.

Lawns
Aerating lawns is best tackled in the fall and early winter. Equipment to remove cores of soil from lawns can be bought or rented and is ideal for large areas. Small lawns, however, are usually aerated by inserting the prongs of garden forks into them. After forking, rake the lawn and brush in a mixture of equal parts sharp sand and potting compost.

19

20

21

◄ Plant outdoor bulbs such as crocuses, muscari, daffodils, narcissus, snowdrops and winter aconites. ►

Above: The brightly faced leopard's bane.

Herbaceous perennials for growing as cut-flowers for room decoration

- ❀ Helenium
  (*Helenium autumnale*)
- ❀ Heliopsis
  (*Heliopsis scabra*)
- ❀ Leopard's Bane
  (*Doronicum*)
- ❀ Lily-of-the-Valley
  (*Convallaria majalis*)
- ❀ Maltese Cross
  (*Lychnis chalcedonica*)
- ❀ Masterwort
  (*Astrantia*)

Organic Gardening

Hoverflies characteristically "hover" in mid-air. A few are pests, but some voraciously feed on aphids. A single hoverfly has been known to eat twenty-one aphids in twenty minutes, while each larva destroys up to 900 aphids in its lifetime.

Vegetables

As soon as crops are harvested, remove the debris so that the soil's surface is bare. Waste left on the soil encourages pests and diseases to linger and spread. Waste known to be contaminated with pests or diseases should be burned.

Greenhouses ▶

A novel way to grow hyacinth bulbs for indoor decoration is in a bulb glass. Fill a bulb glass to its neck with clean water, then put a bulb on top. Place it in a cool, dry, frost-proof shed or cellar until the bulb's roots are 4 inches long and shoots 1 inch out of the neck. Then move indoors and gradually increase the temperature to 64°F.

Greenhouses

Move large exhibition chrysanthemums, currently growing outdoors in pots, into a greenhouse where they will flower.

Lily-of-the-Valley flowers during April and May.

September

22

23

Always wear safety goggles when using chain-saws, trimmers and hedge-clippers.

24

25

When clearing a garden pond in late summer and fall, make the job easier by placing a ladder or long plank over it.

26

27

Check that greenhouse ventilators close properly. During hot summers, wooden ones frequently become distorted and subsequently in winter allow drafts to enter the greenhouse.

28

Freesias that have been in a cold frame must now be taken into a greenhouse. Water the compost and give the plants plenty of light and air.

Flowers
Prepare ground for the planting of herbaceous plants. In cold areas, this task is best left until spring.

Lawns
Bumps and depression in lawns can be eliminated by slicing back the turf and either adding or removing soil.

Vegetables ▲
Pick Brussels sprouts as soon as the buttons are firm. Pick only those that are ready, leaving the others to mature.

Above: Crocuses can be planted this month.

◀ **Fruit**
Plant hybrid berries and blackberries from now until late winter. Space the plants 6-10 feet apart, depending on the variety's vigour. After planting, cut the canes down to about 9 inches high. Now is the time either to check their supporting wires or to provide new ones - it is easier to do this job when plants are small. Provide wires, strained between strong end-posts, 12 inches, 2½ feet and 5 feet above the soil.

Greenhouses
Pot up crocuses (*Crocus chrysanthus*) in late summer. However, unlike daffodils, hyacinths and tulips, which can be given high temperatures and "forced" into flower, crocuses cannot. Pot-up top-sized corms in a pot with holes in its sides and top, using either bulb-fiber or gritty compost. Water the compost and place the pot in a black plastic bag in a cool, frost-proof shed or cellar. When shoots are 1 inch high, move indoors into a cool room. Keep the compost moist - and avoid high temperatures.

Herbaceous perennials for growing as cut-flowers for room decoration

❀ Garden Monkshood
(*Aconitum napellus*)

❀ New York Aster
(*Aster novi-belgii*)

❀ Peruvian Lily
(*Alstroemeria aurea*)

❀ Phlox
(*Phlox paniculata*)

❀ Pyrethrum
(*Pyrethrum roseum*)

New York asters are excellent as cut flowers, as well as for brightening borders in the fall.

Organic Gardening

Green lacewings appear delicate, but are voracious eaters of aphids and other small, soft-bodied insects.

29

30

Always clean garden tools after use and oil bright-metal parts. It extends their lives.

Flowers

Remove early flowers from winter-flowering pansies to encourage the development of larger blooms later in the season.

Flowers

Protect choice alpine plants by placing small cloches or pieces of glass over them. This gives protection from rain. Alpines survive low temperatures, but a combination of water and frost soon kills them.

Pot up daffodil bulbs in late summer and fall, setting them slightly apart and with their noses just above the surface of the compost. Water the compost, allow excess moisture to drain and place the pot in a black plastic bag. Place these in a cool shed or cellar. Periodically, check the compost to insure it is slightly moist, and when shoots are 4 inches high, move indoors and place in a cool position. Slowly increase the temperature from 45°F to 59°F. Keep the compost moist.

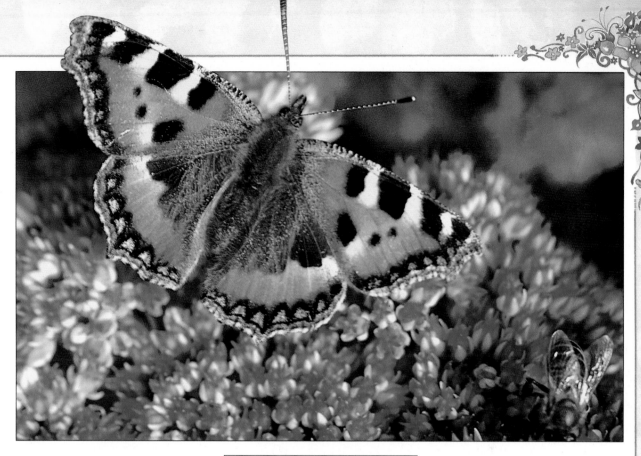

Lawns

Dismantle, clean and pack up garden swings, chairs, tables and children's playthings from lawns and patios. Either place them in a shed or tie a large plastic sheet over them.

Vegetables

Harvest green beans when the pods turn yellow. Also, cut zucchini before the end of the month.

Vegetables ▷

Asparagus crowns planted in April will now have produced tall shoots and fern-like leaves. Cut these down to soil-level and fork lightly between the rows so that soil is left in a slight ridge.

Greenhouses

Check the heating system. If electric, insure it is safe and that a current-breaker device is installed. If a paraffin heater is used, clean wicks and buy fuel in preparation for low temperatures.

Organic Gardening

There are many flowers that attract butterflies in late summer and autumn, such as New York asters, Chinese plumbagos chrysanthemums, showy sedum (*Sedum spectabile*) and heleniums.

Many late summer-flowering plants attract butterflies, such as the small tortoiseshell. Position these plants in a warm, wind-free area.

Herbaceous perennials for growing as cut-flowers for room decoration

❀ Fernleaf Yarrow
   (*Achillea filipendula*)

❀ Shasta Daisy
   (*Chrysanthemum maximum*)

❀ Sneezewort
   (*Achillea ptarmica*)

❀ Tickseed
   (*Coreopsis grandiflora*)

❀ Wide-leaf Sea Lavender
   (*Limonium latifolium*)

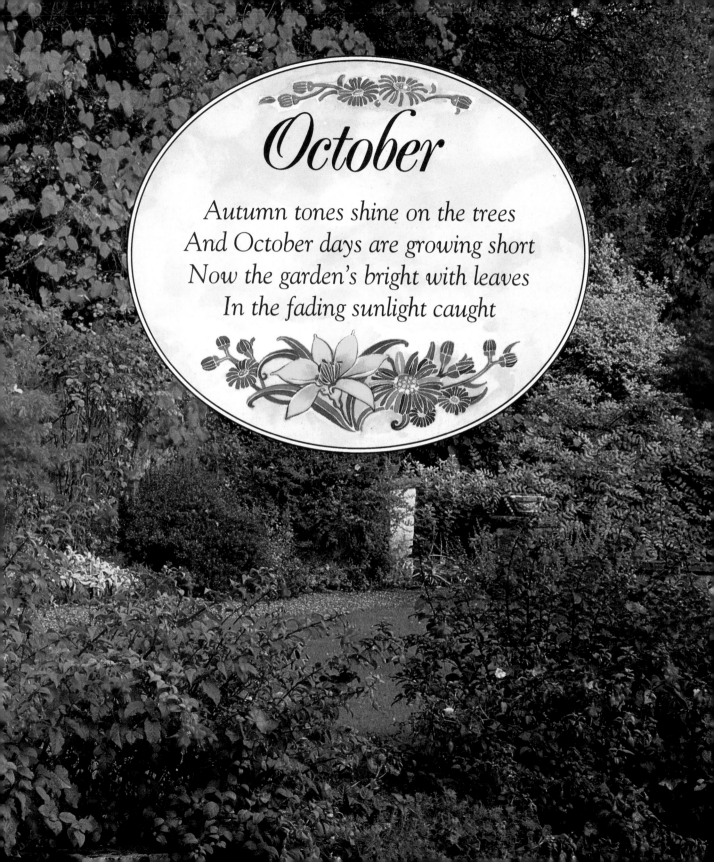

October

Autumn tones shine on the trees
And October days are growing short
Now the garden's bright with leaves
In the fading sunlight caught

October

1

Cut off and burn old potato shoots badly infected with diseases.

2

3

4

Encourage green tomatoes to ripen by wrapping them in paper and placing in drawers.

5

6

7

◀ Tie onions into "ropes" as a way to store them. Hang them in a cool, dry store.

Flowers ▲
Cut the stems of outdoor chrysanthemums that have flowered to 6 inches above soil-level. Use a garden fork to lift the roots (stools), labeling and packing them into boxes. Place them in a cool, frost-proof shed during winter.

Flowers
Complete the planting of spring-flowering bedding plants such as wallflowers and forget-me-nots. Leave a few plants in a nursery bed - or plant a dozen or so in an out-of-the-way corner - so that any plants that die can be replaced in spring. ▼

October is a good month for greenhouse maintenance.

Lawns

After naturalizing daffodils in a lawn, mark out the area so that it is not walked on.

Vegetables ▲

Dig up endive when the leaves die. Cut off the roots and store these in a cellar or cool shed. The roots are later forced to produce fresh shoots.

Fruit

Plant blackcurrants from now and until early spring, whenever the soil is workable. Do not plant them when the soil is frozen or waterlogged. Space the plants 5-6 feet apart, immediately cutting down the shoots to within 2 inches of the soil's surface.

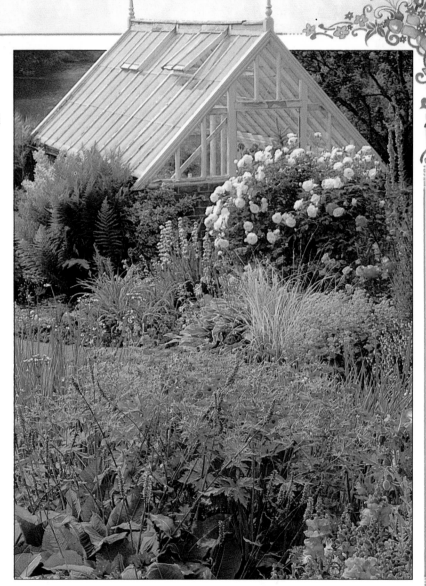

Herbaceous perennials that produce seed heads for room decoration in winter

❀ Baby's Breath
   (*Gypsophila paniculata*)

❀ Bear's Breech
   (*Acanthus mollis*)

❀ Gas Plant
   (*Dictamnus albus*)

Greenhouses

Ventilate greenhouses whenever possible to prevent the build-up of stagnant air and high humidity, which may encourage the presence of diseases.

Greenhouses

Scrub off shading from the outsides of greenhouses. Thoroughly spray the outside with clean water. Also, take down and store roller shades.

Organic Gardening

Don't store potatoes in plastic bags as they create condensation and cause tubers to decay. Preferably, use burlap sacks. Alternatively, employ sacks made from several layers of brown paper. Store them in a cool, frost-proof shed, and cover with an old blanket to exclude light.

8

9

Unless the weather is exceptionally mild, do not trim hedges between now and April.

10

When harvesting trench celery, first use a trowel to remove soil from around their bases, then a garden fork to lever the roots out of the soil. Take care not to damage the stems.

11

12

13

Feed cyclamen plants with a weak liquid fertilizer every two weeks. ▶

14

When digging vegetable plots this fall and winter, do not remove stones. They help to maintain a good soil structure, improve drainage and keep the soil moist in summer.

Flowers

Remove stakes and canes that were used to support plants during summer. Brush off soil, wipe them with a disinfectant and store in a dry shed.

Flowers

Half-ripe cuttings of shrubs - taken earlier in the year and inserted in equal parts moist peat and sharp sand - will now have produced roots. Pot them individually into small pots, and place in a cold frame or cold greenhouse during winter.

Lawns

If the fall has been exceptionally wet, badly drained lawns will now be evident, with water resting on the surface. Install drains now or during winter. Dig narrow trenches in a herringbone fashion, with the end draining into a ditch or large hole filled with rubble. Use either tiles butted together or a trench filled with rubble.

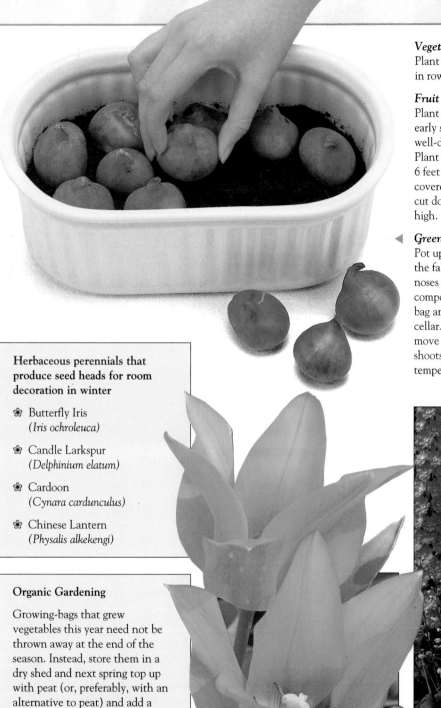

Vegetables
Plant spring cabbages 10-12 inches apart in rows 12 inches apart.

Fruit
Plant raspberry canes from now until early spring. Dig the soil, and mix in well-decayed manure or garden compost. Plant the canes 1½ feet apart in rows 6 feet apart. Insure that each cane is covered by about 3 inches of soil. Then, cut down the stems to 12-15 inches high.

Greenhouses
Pot up tulip bulbs in late summer and the fall, close together and with their noses covered with compost. Water the compost, place the pot in a black plastic bag and put in a cold, frost-proof shed or cellar. When shoots are 2 inches high, move indoors into 45-50°F. Later, when shoots are 4 inches high, raise the temperature to 64°F.

Herbaceous perennials that produce seed heads for room decoration in winter

❀ Butterfly Iris
   (*Iris ochroleuca*)

❀ Candle Larkspur
   (*Delphinium elatum*)

❀ Cardoon
   (*Cynara cardunculus*)

❀ Chinese Lantern
   (*Physalis alkekengi*)

Organic Gardening
Growing-bags that grew vegetables this year need not be thrown away at the end of the season. Instead, store them in a dry shed and next spring top up with peat (or, preferably, with an alternative to peat) and add a sprinkling of a general fertilizer. Plant summer-flowering bedding plants in them.

Candle larkspur *has spire-like flower heads.*

Left: Tulip bulbs can be planted this month.

October

15

16

Lift self-blanching celery for storing.

17

18

Water greenhouse plants only in the morning, so that by nightfall the atmosphere is dry.

19

20

21

Don't feed houseplants in winter unless they are active or flowering. Potted plants which are fed when dormant become soft and prone to pests and diseases.

Flowers ▲

Lift dahlia tubers as soon as their leaves have been blackened by frost. Cut off their stems, about 5 inches above soil-level, and dig up the tubers, taking care not to damage them. Wipe off the soil, and place them upside down in boxes to dry out. Put them in a cool, dry, frost-proof shed. Label each plant.

Lawns

Prepare the ground for new lawns. Dig the area and remove all perennial weeds. Leave the surface with large lumps of soil exposed to the weathering action of winter weather. Prepare an area slightly larger than that required - the edges can be cut back after establishment. In spring, rake the surface level.

Organic Gardening

Organic fertilizers include dried blood, bonemeal, blood, fish and bonemeal, hoof and horn, and seaweed.

Below: The giant-lily is only suitable for growing in large gardens.

Vegetables

Produce winter spinach by placing cloches over late sowings. Place sheets of glass at the ends of the tunnel.

Vegetables

Sow lettuce seeds under cloches or in cold frames by the end of this week, in shallow drills about 6 inches apart. About the middle of December, transplant the young plants into cold frames or cloches, setting them 12 inches apart each way.

Greenhouses

In the fall and winter, giving plants in pots the precise amount of water they need is difficult. This is because plants that are not actively growing do not need much water. Conversely, if too little water is given, leaves become dry and crisp.

Herbaceous perennials that produce seed heads for room decoration in winter

❀ Lamb's Ears
(*Stachys byzantina/S. lanata*)

❀ Giant-Lily
(*Cardiocrinum giganteum*)

❀ Oriental Poppy
(*Papaver orientale*)

❀ Small Globe Thistle
(*Echinop humilis*)

October

22

23

Plant rhubarb crowns from now until November.

24

Examine stored vegetables and remove those showing signs of decay.

25

26

27

Continue to clear up the garden, composting soft materials but burning those contaminated with pests and diseases.

28

Flowers ▲

Clean-up garden ponds, removing dead plants as well as leaves that have fallen in. If there are still large numbers of leaves to fall from nearby trees, place a net or wire-netting over the pond. Waste that remains in the pond decomposes, creating gases detrimental to fish.

Lawns ▶

Rake up leaves. If left on a lawn, they decompose and worms pull them into the soil. Sweep the leaves into heaps, and use two boards, each about 12 inches long and 8 inches wide, to lift them into a wheelbarrow.

Herbaceous perennials that produce seed heads for room decoration in winter

❀ Caucasian Peony
   (*Paeonia mlokosewitschii*)

❀ Common Pearly Everlasting
   (*Anaphalis margaritacea*)

❀ Scotch Cotton-thistle
   (*Onoopordon acanthium*)

❀ Sea Holly
   (*Eryngium maritimum*)

Fruit
Plant red and white currant bushes from now until early spring, setting them 5 feet apart.   ▼

Fruit
Increase blackcurrants by forming 8-inch long cuttings from shoots produced earlier in the year. Insert them 6 inches deep in a nursery bed.

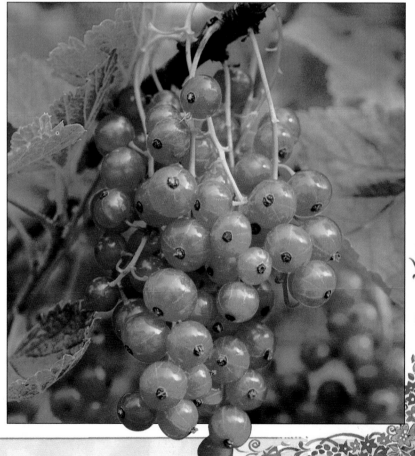

October

29

30

31

Leaves fall off bougainvilleas that are exposed to sudden drops in temperature. Reposition them in 50°F.

In the fall and winter, chain-saws are frequently used to cut trees and branches. Safety is essential, as if misused a chain-saw is a lethal weapon.

- Wear protective goggles.

- Wear a thick jacket with sleeves.

- Don't wear loose clothing or a scarf.

- Don't use the saw above waist height.

- Don't use in rain or on wet wood.

- Keep away from children and animals.

- Don't insert the chain into a previous cut.

- If electrically powered, ensure a circuit-breaker is fitted into the power supply.

The peeling bark of Acer griseum

Flowers

Most houseplant enthusiasts judge if plants need water by looking at the compost or by rubbing a thumb over its surface. If the compost's surface is light colored, it indicates that water is needed. Alternatively, tap clay pots with a thread-spool attached to a cane. If it produces a ringing note, water is needed. If it creates a dull sound, the compost is sufficiently moist.

Lawns

Insure that plants in borders alongside lawns are not overlapping the grass and causing it to die.

Fruit

Increase both red and white currants by taking 1-foot long cuttings from shoots produced during the current year. Remove all but the top four buds on each cutting and insert them 6 inches deep in a nursery bed.

Greenhouses

If one of the sides of your greenhouse is exposed to cold north winds, spread and secure a sheet of clear plastic over it. In exposed areas, long-term protection can be provided by planting a windbreak on the north and east side - but not too close to the greenhouse. Additionally, insulative material can be fixed to the inside of the greenhouse.

Above: Vine leaves *reveal beautiful color in the fall.*

Left: Gladwin iris, whose seed heads make striking indoor arrangements in the fall.

Greenhouses

To give plants better light, put them on shelves in the roof. However, such places are where the temperature decreases most dramatically at night.

Herbaceous perennials that produce seed heads for room decoration in winter

❀ Fernleaf Yarrow
   (*Achillea filipendula*)

❀ Gladwin Iris
   (*Iris foetidissima*)

❀ Wide-Leaf Sea Lavender
   (*Limonium latifolium*)

November

Clear November skies are rare
As like as not fierce storms arrive
But still the garden is not bare
Chrysanthemums the rain survive

November

1

2

Winter is summer's heir.

3

Lift parsnips for storing. Also, dig up winter cabbages: cut off the stumps and place their heads on shelves in a dry, airy shed.

4

Give celery plants a final earthing.

5

6

Clear old runner bean stems and leaves and place them on a compost heap.

7

◀ When repotting prickly cacti, wrap a piece of folded newspaper around them to protect your hands.

Bonfires present a good opportunity to burn garden rubbish, especially plants infected by diseases.

Flowers
When preparing new flower borders, dig the soil 12 inches deep and mix in plenty of well-decayed manure or garden compost. Remove and burn all perennial weeds.

Flowers
Spring-flowering bedding plants that have not been planted in formal beds or in pots and tubs on patios can be set around shrubs to create extra color in spring.

Greenhouses

Protect plants in cold frames by covering them on frosty nights with burlap. Roll it back in the morning, as soon as the frost has gone.

Vegetables ▲

Cut globe artichokes down to soil-level and cover the roots with straw to protect them from severe frost.

Lawns

Lawn cutting is probably over for this year, so thoroughly clean the mower. Scrape off soil and old grass-cuttings, wash the mower and wipe dry. Cover all metal parts with a thin layer of oil or grease, then place the mower in a dry, well-aerated shed. Have electrical parts checked by a competent electrician.

Fruit

Plant gooseberry bushes from now and until early spring, whenever the soil is workable. Space the bushes 5 feet apart.

Fruit ▲

Plant bare-rooted fruit trees from now and until late spring, whenever the soil is not frozen or waterlogged. Dig a large hole and use a fork to loosen the soil in its base, forming it into a slight mound. Place the tree in position, with its roots spread out over the mound. Check its depth by placing a piece of wood across the hole. The old soil mark on the stem should be about 1 inch below the surface. Replace soil around the roots, lifting the tree gently several times to insure soil trickles between them. Firm the soil.

Organic Gardening ▲

A few birds are pests of fruit trees, but some kill the grubs of pests. These birds can be encouraged into your garden by planting shrubs that provide food for them, such as berberis, hawthorn, holly, rowan, sea buckthorn, spindle, viburnum and yew.

November

8

Rake up leaves and place them on a compost heap. If left on paths they become a hazard.

9

10

11

Protect late cauliflowers from frost by bending one or two leaves over the curds.

12

13

14

Harvest leeks by using a garden fork to dig them up. Trim off roots and remove soil.

Flowers
Compost in large tubs often becomes too wet in winter when shrubs and small trees in them are dormant. Place two bricks on the compost around the plant's stem, then cover with clear plastic. The bricks raise the plastic and insure water drains toward the outside of the tub and not to its center. Remove this covering in late winter.

Flowers ▲
Agapanthus growing in tubs needs protection from frost. Cover the plants with 4 inches of straw.

Greenhouses
In winter, water plants in greenhouses very carefully. If plants are excessively watered, their roots die and the foliage wilts. If you are doubtful about a plant needing water, leave it alone. Keeping the compost slightly dry in winter is better that excessive watering, but insure that flowering plants are watered regularly.

Below: The sweetly scented lily-of-the-valley has crowns that can be potted this month for flowering in spring.

Greenhouses ▲

When planting a terrarium, first arrange the plants on a piece of paper shaped like the container's base. At the same time, wipe smooth-surfaced leaves and brush off dust from hairy ones.

Greenhouses

Cut down to 8 inches high chrysanthemum plants that have finished flowering in greenhouses. Burn the leaves and woody stems. Insure that each pot is labeled and keep the compost barely damp.

Everlasting flowers to raise from seeds for room decoration in winter

❀ Cudweed
   (*Gnaphalium*)

❀ Everlasting
   (*Helipterum roseum Acrolinium*)

❀ Globe Amaranth
   (*Gomphrena globosa*)

Greenhouses

Pot up the crowns of lily-of-the-valley (*Convallaria majalis*) to encourage early flowering. Put a few crowns in a 6-inch wide pot, using equal parts sharp sand and loam-based potting compost. Cover the crowns lightly with compost, water them and stand the pots in a cool position. Keep the compost moist but not waterlogged.

15

16

In cold areas, where rose pruning is best left until early spring, shorten top growth now by about a third to reduce the risk of damage from strong winds.

17

18

Greenhouse paths invariably become worn down, slabs subsiding or tilting. Now is the time to reposition them.

19

20

21

Prune established apple trees between now and late winter.

Greenhouses ▲
When planting a terrarium, use a tube of rolled card to insure compost does not dirty the container's sides when filling it.

Flowers
Plant bare-rooted trees and shrubs from now until early spring, whenever the soil is not frozen or waterlogged. Container-grown plants, however, can be planted at anytime, whenever the soil is workable.

Flowers ▶
Plant deciduous hedges formed from bare-rooted plants from now and until early spring. Trim back excessively long or damaged roots, and after planting, cut the plants back by about half to encourage shoots to develop from their bases. If this job is neglected, the hedge will have gaps along its base.

Everlasting flowers to raise from seeds for room decoration in winter

❀ Honesty
  (*Lunaria annua*)

❀ Immortelle
  (*Xeranthemum annuum*)

❀ Matricaria
  (*Matricaria grandiflora*)

Lawns

When digging borders alongside lawns, place a plank on the turf to prevent its edges being broken. Also, if you intend to run a wheelbarrow off the grass and onto the border, use planks to build up the height of the border.

The delicate-looking seed heads of honesty.

Vegetables

Continue to pick Brussels sprouts as soon as their buttons are firm. Also, harvest parsnips, using a garden fork to ease them from the ground. Remove all soil before taking them indoors.

Greenhouses ▶

Encourage African violets (*Saintpaulia ionantha*) to develop roots by suspending the ends of their leaf stalks (petioles) in water. Fill a small bottle with clean water, wrap a piece of paper over the top, pierce a hole in it and push a leaf stalk through, so that its end is in the water. When the stem develops roots, pot up singly into small pots.

November

22

Paint fences with a wood preservative now that leaves have fallen and plants do not obstruct them.

23

24

25

Clean edging-irons, lawn rakes and edging-shears. Wipe bright metal surfaces with an oily cloth.

26

27

28

Harvest winter cabbages as soon as they are firm and mature.

Flowers
Fork lightly between shrubs, taking care not to damage their roots. Dig up and burn perennial weeds - if their roots are left, they will grow again during the following year.

Flowers
Tender shrubs in tubs on patios benefit from a covering of straw or hay during the coldest part of the year. Cold winds soon damage tender leaves. Protect shrubs by inserting five canes into the compost around the tub's edges, tying them at the top, arranging straw or hay around them and securing it with a spiral of string. Remove the covering when the risk of frost damage passes.

Flowers
Place cloches over Christmas roses (*Helleborus niger*) to protect their flowers from heavy raindrops falling on muddy ground and then splashing on the flowers.

Fruit

Regularly check apples and pears earlier put in a storage shed. Remove those that are showing signs of decay. If left, they encourage other fruits to rot.

Fruit

Before planting new apple trees, check that they are compatible with existing varieties. All apples need pollen from another variety to pollinate them.

Greenhouses

Houseplants with colorful foliage are particularly welcome in the fall and winter. They can be displayed in indoor hanging baskets, and are either planted in the container or left in their pots. First, plan the design by arranging the plants on a piece of paper the size and shape of the container.

Indoor hanging baskets bring color in winter.

Left: The Christmas rose flowers in winter.

Organic Gardening

Moles eat pests such as crane flies, wireworms and millepedes. Although they also eat worms - which are essential to gardens - it is foolish to kill them.

Everlasting flowers to raise from seeds for room decoration in winter

❀ Poppy
  (*Papaver* 'Gigantic Podded')

❀ Scabious
  (*Scabiosa stellata* 'Drumstick')

❀ Statice
  (*Limonium sinuatum*)

29

Christmas presents are only a few weeks away, so drop hints about the gardening tools you need!

30

Where young conifers grown as specimen plants have developed two leader shoots, cut out one of them.

Flowers

If the previous summer was hot and many of your plants suffered from lack of water, consider growing drought-resistant plants and mulching the area with shingle or small stones.

Flowers

Keep cyclamen and azaleas tidy by removing dead flowers. With cyclamen, pull off the flower stems intact, but for azaleas just nip off the dead flowers. ▼

Flowers

Bare-rooted trees and shrubs ordered through the mail may arrive when the soil is frozen or waterlogged. They therefore cannot be planted immediately. Either place them in a cool, airy shed, or unpack them completely and put the roots in a trench in the garden, covering with soil.

Flowers

Insure that tubs on patios are raised on three bricks. If stood directly on the ground, it encourages the tub's base to rot.

Vegetables

Don't be tempted to retain a few potato tubers for replanting next year - they will probably be infected by viruses and therefore will not produce a good crop. Instead, buy fresh seed potatoes, certified free from viruses.

Greenhouses

When planning a greenhouse, position it to receive the maximum light. It should also be sheltered from cold winds.
Insure that the door faces south or west, so that cold winds do not blow directly into it.

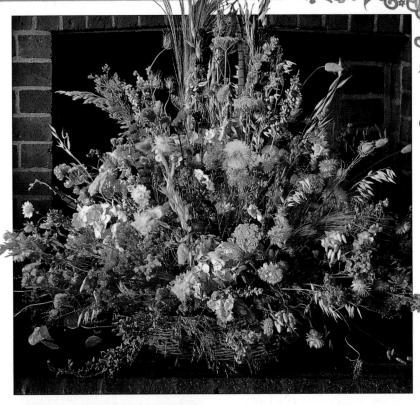

Right: A colorful dried-flower arrangement. This display enriches homes in winter, at a time when there is little other color.

Below: Strawflowers, pretty in gardens during summer and perfect in dried flower arrangements.

Everlasting flowers to raise from seeds for room decoration in winter

❀ Statice
   (*Limonium aureum*)

❀ Strawflower
   (*Helichrysum bracteatum*)

❀ Winged Everlasting
   (*Ammobium alatum
   "Grandiflorum"*)

Organic Gardening

Bats are beneficial to gardeners, eating half their own weight of insects at night. Do not interfere with their resting places.

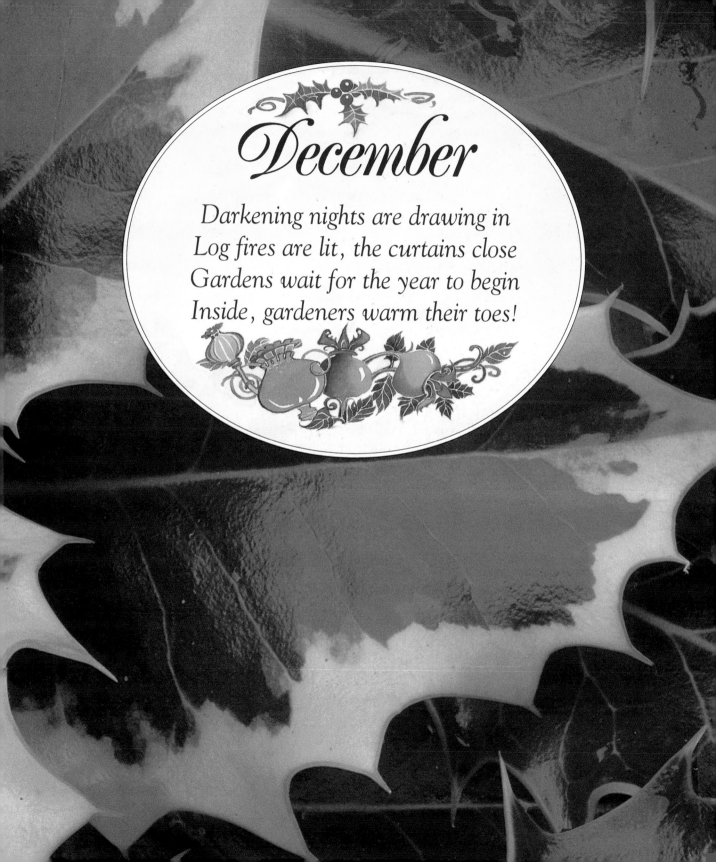

December

Darkening nights are drawing in
Log fires are lit, the curtains close
Gardens wait for the year to begin
Inside, gardeners warm their toes!

December

1

If the branches of a neighbor's tree extend over your garden, talk to your neighbor to avoid misunderstandings before cutting the tree.

2

3

4

Poinsettias flower at Christmas, but once their display is over they are best discarded. ▶

5

6

7

◀ Don't allow azaleas to become dry - keep their compost moist at all times.

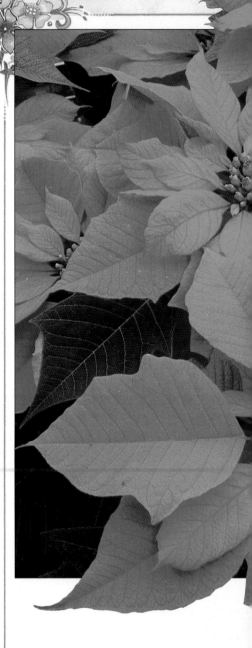

Flowers

Evergreen shrubs and climbers with variegated leaves bring welcome color during winter. Climbers such as the Persian ivy (*Hedera colchica*) Algerian ivy (*Hedera canariensis*) and the

Flowers
Prune roses at any time from now until early spring. In cold areas it is better to postpone this job until spring.

Lawns
If you are considering buying a new lawn mower, now is the time to look around for bargains. If your lawn is surrounded by flower beds, a roller type is a good buy, whereas if the lawn is edged with stones a hover type is better as it easily rides over stones that may not be level with the lawn's surface.

Herbaceous perennials with attractive leaves for use in flower arrangements

❀ Bear's Breech
   (*Acanthus mollis*)

❀ Bishop's Hat
   (*Epimedium grandiflorum*)

❀ Catmint
   (*Nepeta faassennii*)

❀ Hybrid Astilbe
   (*Astilbe x arendsii*)

Above: Astilbes are fluffy-flowered perennials.

Vegetables
Plant endive roots in large pots of sand. Water them and place in a warm, dark position, about 45°F. Later, shoots develop from their tops.

Fruit
Prune red and white currants from now and until early spring.

Greenhouses
Keep temperatures at a minimum as the cost of heating increases dramatically for each degree rise in warmth. However, do not leave the greenhouse totally closed - ventilation is essential.

small-leaved English ivy (*Hedera helix*) attractively clothe walls. Variegated shrubs for borders include many hollies, the Japanse aucuba (*Aucuba japonica*) and some attractive varieties of *Elaeagnus pungens*.

December

8

9

10

11

Do not walk on soil unnecessarily as it causes compaction and damages its structure.

12

13

14

When calculating the number of fish you can comfortably have in your pond, reckon on about ½ inch of fish for every 2½ gallons of water.

Flowers
Cover tender herbaceous plants with straw to prevent frost damaging their roots.

Flowers
Repair fences, using either angled metal or blocks of wood. Insure the tops of the posts are either sloped or fitted with caps to protect the end grain from excessive water.

Vegetables
Continue to harvest leeks and parsnips.

Fruit
Inspect stakes supporting fruit trees, as well as posts and wires for cordon fruits. Replace damaged or broken supports.

Fruit
Check the ties on fruit and ornamental trees to insure they are not broken or strangling the trunks. Either use a piece of burlap sacking folded several times and secured with strong string, or a proprietary plastic tie that can be easily adjusted as the tree grows.

Organic Gardening

Traditionally, in mild areas shallots are planted on the shortest day of the year (December 22) and harvested on the longest (June 21). Most people, however, wait until February before planting them. Leave their necks just above the surface.

Greenhouses

If the greenhouse is empty, thoroughly clean it. Use a small piece of bent wire to remove dirt from between the overlaps of glass. Scrub the framework and glass. Thoroughly wash with clean water. Also, scrub the staging. If possible, leave the door and ventilators open for a few days, especially if the weather is very cold.

Right: Lady's mantle has attractive leaves.

Below: Allegheny foam-flowers are superb in gardens, as well as in flower arrangements.

Greenhouses

Keep the glass clean. Dirty glass in winter can reduce the amount of light available to plants by 50 percent.

Herbaceous perennials with attractive leaves for use in flower arrangements

- ❀ Allegheny Foam-flower (*Tiarella cordifolia*)
- ❀ Day Lily (*Hemerocallis*)
- ❀ Fennel (*Foeniculum vulgare*)
- ❀ Lady's Mantle (*Alchemilla mollis*)

Left: Fennel's delicate leaves.

December

15

16

Christmastide
Comes in like a bride,
With Holly and Ivy clad.

17

18

When planning to buy a greenhouse,
insure it has several ventilators. The total
area of ventilators should be at least
20 percent of the floor area.

19

20

When planning a new fence or wall,
check with your town council to insure
you do not erect one too high.

21

Flowers ▲
When cutting evergreen foliage from the
garden for indoor Christmas decorations,
use sharp pruning shears and cut to just
above a bud. This insures that short,
unsightly spurs are not left on a plant. Such
stubs also encourage the onset of decay.

Flowers
The roots of Christmas trees are best
stood in a bucket of water for several
days before the tree is taken indoors.
This helps the tree to retain its needles
and freshness for a longer period.

Lawns ▶
Brush lawns to remove dead grass and
fallen leaves, as well as to scatter
wormcasts. However, if the surface is
wet or frosted, wait until the weather
improves.

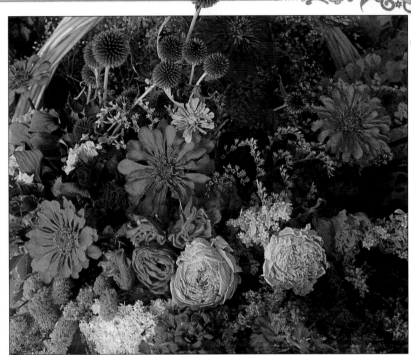

Above: A basket of dried flowers, which makes a lovely winter gift.

Vegetables

Harvest turnips and rutabagas, carefully lifting them with a garden fork. Remove all soil before taking them indoors.

Fruit

Inspect fruits in store regularly, removing those showing signs of decay.

Greenhouses

Water cyclamen plants carefully, taking care not to wet their leaves and flowers. Pull off dead flowers - complete with their stems.

Herbaceous perennials with attractive leaves for use in flower arrangements

❀ Lamb's Ears
(*Stachys byzantina*)

❀ London Pride
(*Saxifraga umbrosa*)

❀ Meadow Rue
(*Thalictrum*)

❀ Mullein
(*Verbascum bombyciferum*)

Organic Gardening

If honey fungus infests shrub borders, plant resistant types such bamboo, elaeagnus, holly, mahonia, tamarisk, thorn and yew.

December

22

23

Holly berries shining red,
Mean a long winter, 'tis said.

24

25

26

27

Brush up the last of the leaves, putting them on a compost heap.

28

When planting a hedge, do not position the stems of the plants exactly along the boundary line. Instead, set them to half of the hedge's expected width in from the boundary.

Flowers
Remove leaves from rock gardens. If left, they retain moisture around plants, and encourage stems and leaves to decay.

Flowers
Re-firm the soil around newly-planted roses, fruit and ornamental trees and shrubs. It will be necessary to undertake this task several times before the arrival of spring.

Fruit
In areas where rabbits are pests, insure that wire netting or plastic guards have been fitted around trunks. Young trees are usually the first ones to be attacked, and if totally girdled are killed.

Fruit ▲
Check posts supporting fruit trees. If a vertical post has rotted away, re-support the tree with one driven in at an angle of 45 degrees, so that its head crosses the trunk. The head of the stake should be into the prevailing wind. Alternatively, drive two vertical stakes into the ground, about 12 inches on either side of the tree, and secure a cross support to them and the tree.

Fruit
When using pruning shears, do not strain and buckle the blades by cutting thick branches. To cut thick branches, use either a saw or lopping shears with long handles.

Organic Gardening

If you have couch grass in your vegetable patch, do not use a rotovator to cultivate the soil as this will chop up the underground stems and make the problem worse.

Greenhouses

Cut down the last of the late-flowering chrysanthemums growing in pots, severing the stems about 6 inches above the pots. Remove and burn the stems and leaves, label the plants and keep the compost barely moist.

Greenhouses

Pot up hippeastrum bulbs individually into 5-6-inch pots, using potting compost. Leave half the bulb exposed, water the compost and place the pot in 55-61°F.

Herbaceous perennials with attractive leaves for use in flower arrangements

❀ Common Pearly Everlasting
(*Anaphalis margaritacea*)

❀ Plantain Lily
(*Hosta*)

❀ Rue
(*Ruta graveolens* "Jackman's Blue")

❀ Sea Holly
(*Eryngium maritimum*)

Above: A Christmas wreath, perfect for a front door where it is able to welcome guests.

Below: Hippeastrum flowers are spectacular and in many colors – white, pink and red.

December

29

30

Before using any chemical in the garden read the instructions carefully - and do not adjust the recommended concentrations.

Below: Winter sweet (chimonanthus praecox), a shrub guaranteed to bring color and scent to a winter garden.

31

When cutting off large branches from trees, first cut about halfway through from underneath. This prevents the bark tearing downward when later cut from above.

Ponds

Ponds can be given an added quality in evening and at night by the installation of submerged lights and spotlights. Although lights cannot be fitted until spring, now is the time to dig a trench to take the power cable from the house to the pond. First, however, consult an electrician about its position and depth.

Flowers

Winter-flowering shrubs brighten gardens when there is little other color in the garden except for variegated evergreen shrubs. Position them where they can be seen from a window, while those with scented flowers are best planted near a path.

Greenhouses

Small, electrically heated propagation frames are well worth buying for raising plants in late winter and early spring. They enable seeds to be sown in warmth without having to heat the entire greenhouse.

Fruit ▶

If you have an old apple tree, with branches too high for the fruits to be easily picked, it can be topworked. Although this is a little used technique, during winter cut back branches to about 3 feet of the trunk. Pieces of the desired variety are then inserted into the bark around the cuts - three or four on each branch.

Above left: Cornus stolonifera "Flaviramea" has bright yellow shoots in winter.

Above: Hamamelis mollis 'Pallida' bears eye-catching, lemon-yellow flowers in winter.

Herbaceous perennials with attractive leaves for use in flower arrangements

❀ Golden Dead Nettle
   (*Lamiastrum galeobdolon*)

❀ Lanceleaf Figwort
   (*Scrophularia Lanceolata*)

❀ Western Sage
   (*Artemisia ludoviciana*)

❀ White Mugwort
   (*Artemisia lactiflora*)

❀ Yarrow
   (*Achillea taygetea*)

The Wild Garden

Wild gardens have for many years been mainly formed of azaleas, border primulas and other "choice" plants from foreign lands. Today, however, the trend is to naturalize native plants in parts of our gardens so that with butterflies and birds they create a real wild garden.

Native plants, so long dismissed because of their common nature, often have just as much eye-appeal as expensive foreign introductions. Seed catalogs list native plants, either on their own or in mixtures.

Butterflies can be encouraged by planting wild flowers that appeal to them. Cultivated border plants also encourage their presence and many are suggested earlier in this book, during spring, summer and the fall.

Wild flowers that attract butterflies and bees

- ❀ Bird's Foot Trefoil
  (*Lotus scoparius*)
- ❀ Bouncing Bet
  (*Saponaria officinalis*)
- ❀ Butter-and-eggs
  (*Linaria vulgaris*)
- ❀ Cuckoo Bittercross
  (*Cardamine pratensis*)
- ❀ English Bluebell
  (*Endymion non-scriptus*)
- ❀ Field Scabious
  (*Knautia arvensis*)
- ❀ Johnny-jump up
  (*Viola tricolor*)
- ❀ Knapweed
  (*Centaurea nigra*)
- ❀ Ox-eye Daisy
  (*leucanthemum chryscnthemum*)
- ❀ Purple Loosestrife
  (*Lythrum salicaria*)
- ❀ Ragged Robin
  (*Lychnis flos-cuculi*)
- ❀ Wild Thyme
  (*Thymus serpyllum*)
- ❀ Vervain
  (*Verbena officinalis*)

Left: Primula veris is a meadow flower. Some seed companies offer seeds of this primula, as well as English primroses (Primula vulgaris). Once established, these primulas will flower for many years.

Below: It is easier to establish a large wild flower meadow than one that is small, as it enables larger areas of each species to be grown. The grass creates an attractive backdrop to the flowers. In large wild gardens, create meandering paths by mowing the grass, but take care not to cut other areas until after most of the flowers have flowered and scattered their seeds.

Providing birds with water

Birds need water for both drinking and bathing. Purpose-built bird baths can be bought, but an alternative is to invert an old metal garbage can lid, support it on bricks and fill with water. A nightlight placed underneath in winter prevents total freezing. Do not put salt or antifreeze in the water.

Encouraging garden birds

To many gardeners, birds are an important part of their garden and frequently need encouragement, especially in winter when food and water are difficult to obtain. Fortunately, many households put out food in winter. Food to provide includes:

- Crumbled bread, moistened if dry.

- Bird seed sold in proprietary mixtures. Sunflower seeds appeal to small European finches while seeds such as millet attract finches and common hedge sparrows.

- Stale cake and cookies.

- Fruit, such as windfalls or bruised apples and pears, appeals to thrushes and blackbirds. Dried fruits, such as raisins, can be used but these must first be soaked in water.

- Cheese, crumbled or grated, is tempting for North American thrushes and wrens.

- Fat from bacon rinds or chops. Hang from a tree branch.

- Fresh coconut appeals to titmice. Put out pieces of it, perhaps hung from branches. However, do not offer birds shredded coconut.

- Peanuts, rich in fat, attract titmices; English sparrows; nuthatches, and pine siskins.

- Nuts, crushed or chopped, appeal to hedge sparrows and North American thrushes.

Remember ...

- ❀ Don't dead-head plants in the fall as this often removes seeds that birds could eat.

- ❀ Using pesticides kills insects that birds might otherwise eat. Encourage birds into your garden to eat aphids and other pests.

- ❀ In the fall, leave part of your garden untidy, so that birds can rummage through leaves to find food.

- ❀ Thrushes, hedge sparrows and wrens like to feed on the ground, so scatter food on the lawn, but away from bushes where cats may hide.

- ❀ Don't put food on the ground late in the day as it may remain uneaten and could attract rats and mice.

- ❀ Bird tables are relatively safe places for many birds.

- ❀ Seed-eating birds, such as small finches have difficulty in finding seeds in early spring, so put out food for them.

- ❀ When the ground is frozen, worms are difficult for blackbirds and thrushes to find, so put out food for them.

Safety and time-saving tips

Using chemicals safely

Chemicals can be safely used indoors and in the garden if a few precautions are taken:

- First, read the label on the bottle or package.

- Double check chemicals used on vegetables, especially the time between spraying and harvesting.

- Do not experiment with concentrations - follow those recommended. And do not mix one chemical with another, except when recommended.

- Check that the chemical is right for the plant and the problem it is to control.

- Do not keep any chemical except in its original container - never put it in containers that appeal to children.

- Store chemicals out of reach of children and pets. And when mixing, keep them away.

- Keep plant-eating animals such as guinea pigs and rabbits off newly-sprayed greenery until it is dry or after it has been cut.

- Avoid contaminating fish ponds, swimming pools and bird baths, as well as fish tanks indoors.

- Take houseplants outdoors and place them in plastic bags to spray them. This insures that delicate fabrics and wallpapers are not damaged.

- Wash your hands after using garden chemicals.

- If garden chemicals splash in your eyes, seek medical advice immediately, taking the chemical and its packaging (in a plastic bag) with you.

Electrical safety in the garden

Electricity in the garden has made gardening easier and more enjoyable, but it must be treated with respect.

- Never use a piece of equipment that is not connected to the mains supply through a current-breaker (also known as a power breaker) device. This immediately shuts off the power if a piece of equipment is faulty, has frayed cord, or loose connections.

- Have electrical equipment serviced every year by a competent electrician.

- Don't use electrical equipment in the wet.

- Only use cords, sockets and plugs in the garden that are approved for outdoor use.

- Turn off the power at the mains before adjusting any equipment.

The "unthinking" accidents

Many accidents in gardens appear "just to happen", but most are avoidable.

- Don't leave tools all over the garden - keep them where you are working. When not in use, push garden forks into the soil, and do not leave rakes so that if stepped on, the handle flies up and hits you.

- Wear protective clothing and gloves when using powered equipment.

- Each year, many gardeners lose their sight or have an eye damaged through dust, dirt and wood splinters piercing them. Always use protective goggles when using powered equipment. Also, beware of bending down and poking an eye with the top of a cane or stake.

- Wear gloves to protect your hands from dirt, especially when dealing with compost heaps that might have been infected by rats.

Quick tips

Levelling: To assess the general levels in a garden, insert a piece of clear, tubular plastic into each end of a hosepipe, then fill it with water. Secure one end to a short, upright post, with its top at the desired height. The equivalent height is indicated by the water-level at the other end.

Creating flowers beds: Use canes and string to mark out flower beds before cutting them.

Estimating a tree's height: Fix a 3¼ft long piece of wood at 45 degrees to the top of a 6ft long pole. Hold the pole upright and look along the angled piece of wood until it aligns with the tree's top. The height of the tree is the distance from the trunk to the pole, plus 6ft.

An A to Z of gardening 'phone lines

Bedding plant specialists

....

....

....

Building materials

....

....

Bulb specialists

....

....

Children's swings and garden equipment

....

....

Conservatory manufacturers

....

....

Do-it-yourself centers

....

....

Fencing contractors

....

....

Fencing materials and gates

....

....

Fruit trees and bushes

....

....

Furniture and ornaments

....

....

Garden centers

....

....

....

Garden shed manufacturers

....

....

Garden shed erectors

....

....

Garden tool suppliers

....

....

Glass suppliers

....

....

Grass – contract cutting companies

....

....

Greenhouse manufacturers and suppliers

....

....

Greenhouse plants

....

....

Herb specialists

....

....

Houseplant specialists

....

....

Landscape designers

....

....

Lawn mowers – servicing and maintenance

....

....

Ornaments for the garden

....

....

Paraffin suppliers

....

....

Patio plant specialists

....

....

....

Pots – ornamental

....

....

Rock garden plant specialists

....

....

Seed specialists

....

....

Shrub specialists

....

....

Tools – rental stores

....

....

Tree surgeons

....

....

Turfing services

....

....

Waste removal contractors

....

....

Water garden specialists

....

....

....